No. 10953

**Ideal
School Supply
Company**
®

Grades 4-6

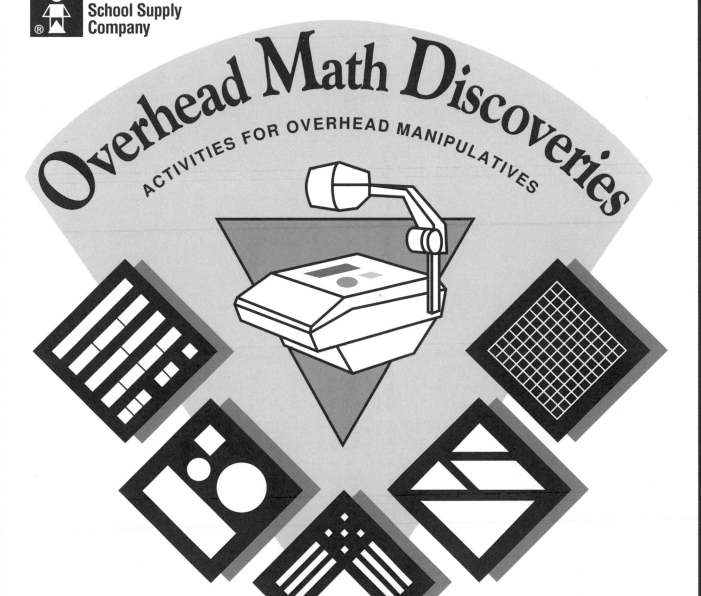

Overhead Math Discoveries
ACTIVITIES FOR OVERHEAD MANIPULATIVES

- Geoboard
- Tangrams
- Attribute Blocks
- Base Ten Blocks
- Fraction Builder™
- Hundred Number Board

Judy Goodnow
Shirley Hoogeboom

Overhead Math Discoveries: Activities for Manipulatives, Grades 4-6

◆

Cover design by Virginia Sanders

Illustrations by Laurie Laumeister

Technical Illustrations by Joe Parenteau and Sherri Takahara

Graphic Design by Nancy Tseng

© 1993 Ideal School Supply Company
Oak Lawn, Illinois 60453
Printed in U.S.A.

ISBN: 1-56451-058-1

2 3 4 5 6 7 8 9 10. 9 7 6 5 4 3

Contents

Activities for Overhead Base Ten Blocks

Activities for Overhead Hundred Number Boards

Activities for Overhead Fraction Builder™

Activities for Overhead Tangrams

Activities for Overhead Geoboards

Activities for Overhead Attribute Blocks

Blackline Masters for Overhead Transparencies

Notes to the Teacher

Overhead Math Discoveries is a set of two teacher resource books of activities for using manipulatives on the overhead projector. The books are:

Overhead Math Discoveries: Activities With Manipulatives, Grades 1-3
Overhead Math Discoveries: Activities With Manipulatives, Grades 4-6

Each book presents 36 activities—six for each of six different manipulatives. In each activity, an illustration shows how to arrange the manipulative pieces on the overhead projector. Instructions are given for posing puzzle-like problems for the children to solve. Sample questions are included to encourage children to think through the problems and talk about their discoveries. The resources also include 12 blackline masters for overhead transparencies.

The activities are designed to spark the children's curiosity about math, and to provide experiences in which they can make their own discoveries about numbers and geometric shapes. As children explore with manipulatives and solve problems, they deepen their understanding of math concepts and strengthen their math and thinking skills. The activities emphasize counting, number sense, place value, patterns and relationships, whole number operations, money, geometry, and measurement.

Suggestions for Using *Overhead Math Discoveries: Activities With Manipulatives, Grades 4-6*

Overhead Activities. Each activity is presented on two pages. The first page lists the materials that you will need and illustrates how to set up the manipulative pieces on the overhead projector. The second page describes how you can pose the problems and motivate your students to participate in finding solutions. Suggestions are also given for questions you can ask after the activity. The purpose of these questions is to encourage students to think about what they discovered while trying to solve the problems, and to communicate their ideas to you and to their classmates. Finally, ideas are included for ways in which the children can continue exploring, often creating their own problems for others to solve.

Student-Participation Techniques. Certain techniques, described below, are used in the activities to engage all of the students in problem solving!

- Covering part or all of the manipulative pieces on the projector injects suspense into the activities and appeals to children's fondness for mystery! This technique can also focus the students' attention on a particular piece that is being shown on the screen. Usually a sheet of blank paper is used for the cover-up.

- Asking students to record their estimates or numbers or drawings on "Think Sheets" or dot paper keeps students involved. Scratch paper serves very well for Think Sheets, but giving it the special name suggests that it is important for keeping track of one's thinking while solving problems! Pencils or crayons are used for recording on Think Sheets.

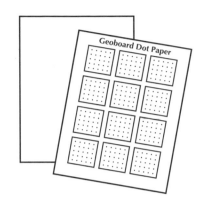

- Giving strips of an overhead transparency to each group of children is a technique that invites all of the students to become actively engaged in solving a puzzle shown on the screen. The transparency strips give information which the students relate to something being shown on the screen.

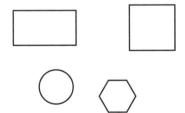

- Giving overhead pieces to each group of children is a technique that invites all of the children to become actively engaged in solving a puzzle shown on the screen. Some activities suggest that a set of overhead pieces be divided in a particular way, then distributed to small groups of students.

Preparing for the Activities. You may want to make overhead transparencies of some or all of the blackline masters on pages 80-91. Some activities also suggest making paper copies of these masters for the students to use as recording sheets.

Grouping the Students. Cooperative learning is emphasized in the activities, so suggestions are often made to have students work together in pairs or in small groups of four to six. You can present the activities to an entire class, or to smaller groups of children.

Presenting the Activities. The activities can be used in any order that is appropriate for your students. In this book, the activities are presented in sections, by manipulative, and are generally sequenced according to level of difficulty within the section. These overhead activities fit with any math program that you are using with your students. You can use them to extend specific math lessons, or as problems of the day or week, or simply to enrich your students' math experiences.

When you have selected an activity, prepare the materials listed and described at the beginning of the instructions, then set up the manipulative pieces on the overhead projector as shown in the illustration.

The *Solving Problems* section of an activity suggests a way for you to pose problems, and to lead the children to think about them and solve them. You can modify these instructions as necessary for your students. You may want to make up additional problems and extend the lesson to another day.

The *Talking About Discoveries* section provides some questions that you can ask your students to help them reflect on what they discovered and learned as they did the activity, and to encourage them to articulate their ideas to you and to their classmates.

In the *Solving More Problems* sections, suggestions are given for ways in which the children can continue exploring, often creating their own problems for others to solve. If possible, provide the children with sets of the regular manipulatives designed for classroom use. The Attribute Blocks and Base Ten sets have more pieces and give the students greater flexibility. Encourage students to share their problems and solutions with the class or a small group, using the overhead projector. When students are going to demonstrate a problem on the projector, be sure to have them check and see if there are enough pieces in the overhead set to show their problem or solution.

The following symbols are used in the lessons for Attribute Blocks:

Shapes: ☐ ⬡ ◯ ▭ △

Color and Size: Y = large yellow   y = small yellow
                 B = large blue   b = small blue
                 R = large red   r = small red

Example: (B) = large blue circle

Related Manipulatives and Materials Available from Ideal School Supply

Base Ten Blocks for the Overhead Projector, ID7595
Base Ten Blocks, Plastic, ID7570, ID7571, ID7572, ID7569
Base Ten Blocks, Wood, ID7551, ID7552, ID7553, ID7554
Base Ten Rubber Stamps, ID7574
Base Ten Activity Cards: Counting, ID7561
Base Ten Activity Cards: Showing Numbers, ID7562

Hundred Number Board for the Overhead Projector, 1-100, with Colored Squares, ID3540
Hundred Number Board for the Overhead Projector, 0-99, with Colored Squares, ID3541
Hundred Number Board for the Overhead Projector, Blank, with 0-100 Number Tiles, ID3542
Hundred Number Tiles for the Overhead Projector, ID3543 and ID3544
Hundred Number Board, 1-100, ID33160
Hundred Number Board, 0-99, ID33161
Hundred Number Board, with Number Tiles 1-100, ID3175
100 Activities for the Hundred Number Board, ID33121

Fraction Builder™ for the Overhead Projector, ID7655 and ID32105
Fraction Builder™, ID7645
Fraction Builder™: Naming Fractions, ID7646
Fraction Builder™: Comparing Fractions, ID7647
Fraction Builder™: Addition, ID7648
Fraction Builder™: Subtraction, ID7649

Tangrams for the Overhead Projector, ID7964
Tangrams, ID7957 and 7965
Tangram Templates, ID34184
Puzzlers for Overhead Tangrams, ID7961
Tangram Pattern Cards, ID7962

Geoboard for the Overhead Projector, 5 x 5 Pin, ID7539
Circle Geoboard for the Overhead Projector, ID7533
Geoboards, 5 x 5 Pin, ID7537 and ID7538
Geoboards, 5 x 5 Pin/Circle, ID7534 and ID7535
Geoboards, 11 x 11 Pin, ID7531 and ID7536
Demonstration Geoboard, ID7530
Geoboard Activity Sheets, ID7543
Mathcards for Geoboards: Geometric Shapes, ID75411
Mathcards for Geoboards: Shapes and Angles, ID75412
Puzzlers for Overhead Geoboards, ID34019

Attribute Blocks for the Overhead Projector, ID6257
Attribute Blocks, ID3185, ID3186, and ID3187
Attribute Blocks Stickers, ID30422
Attribute Blocks Templates, ID34188
Attribute Logic Block Activities, ID30425

Equivalent Fractions, Percents, and Decimals

Fractions	Equivalent Fractions	Equivalent Percents	Equivalent Decimals
$\frac{1}{2}$	$\frac{2}{4}$ $\frac{3}{6}$ $\frac{4}{8}$ $\frac{5}{10}$ $\frac{6}{12}$	50%	$0.50
$\frac{2}{2}$	$\frac{3}{3}$ $\frac{4}{4}$ $\frac{5}{5}$ $\frac{6}{6}$ $\frac{8}{8}$ $\frac{10}{10}$ $\frac{12}{12}$	100%	1.00
$\frac{1}{3}$	$\frac{2}{6}$ $\frac{4}{12}$	33.3%	0.333
$\frac{2}{3}$	$\frac{4}{6}$ $\frac{8}{12}$	66.6%	0.666
$\frac{3}{3}$	$\frac{2}{2}$ $\frac{4}{4}$ $\frac{5}{5}$ $\frac{6}{6}$ $\frac{8}{8}$ $\frac{10}{10}$ $\frac{12}{12}$	100%	1.00
$\frac{1}{4}$	$\frac{2}{8}$ $\frac{3}{12}$	25%	0.25
$\frac{2}{4}$	$\frac{1}{2}$ $\frac{3}{6}$ $\frac{4}{8}$ $\frac{5}{10}$ $\frac{6}{12}$	50%	0.50
$\frac{3}{4}$	$\frac{6}{8}$ $\frac{9}{12}$	75%	0.75
$\frac{4}{4}$	$\frac{2}{2}$ $\frac{3}{3}$ $\frac{5}{5}$ $\frac{6}{6}$ $\frac{8}{8}$ $\frac{10}{10}$ $\frac{12}{12}$	100%	1.00
$\frac{1}{5}$	$\frac{2}{10}$	20%	0.20
$\frac{2}{5}$	$\frac{4}{10}$	40%	0.40
$\frac{3}{5}$	$\frac{6}{10}$	60%	0.60
$\frac{4}{5}$	$\frac{8}{10}$	80%	0.80
$\frac{5}{5}$	$\frac{2}{2}$ $\frac{3}{3}$ $\frac{4}{4}$ $\frac{6}{6}$ $\frac{8}{8}$ $\frac{10}{10}$ $\frac{12}{12}$	100%	1.00
$\frac{1}{6}$	$\frac{2}{12}$	16.6%	0.166
$\frac{2}{6}$	$\frac{4}{12}$	33.3%	0.333
$\frac{3}{6}$	$\frac{1}{2}$ $\frac{2}{4}$ $\frac{4}{8}$ $\frac{5}{10}$ $\frac{6}{12}$	50%	0.50
$\frac{4}{6}$	$\frac{2}{3}$ $\frac{8}{12}$	66.6%	0.666
$\frac{5}{6}$	$\frac{10}{12}$	83.3%	0.833
$\frac{6}{6}$	$\frac{2}{2}$ $\frac{3}{3}$ $\frac{4}{4}$ $\frac{5}{5}$ $\frac{8}{8}$ $\frac{10}{10}$ $\frac{12}{12}$	100%	1.00
$\frac{1}{8}$		12.5%	0.125
$\frac{2}{8}$	$\frac{1}{4}$ $\frac{3}{12}$	25%	0.25
$\frac{3}{8}$		37.5%	0.375
$\frac{4}{8}$	$\frac{1}{2}$ $\frac{2}{4}$ $\frac{3}{6}$ $\frac{5}{10}$ $\frac{6}{12}$	50%	0.50
$\frac{5}{8}$		62.5%	0.625
$\frac{6}{8}$	$\frac{3}{4}$ $\frac{9}{12}$	75%	0.75
$\frac{7}{8}$		87.5%	0.875
$\frac{8}{8}$	$\frac{2}{2}$ $\frac{3}{3}$ $\frac{4}{4}$ $\frac{5}{5}$ $\frac{6}{6}$ $\frac{10}{10}$ $\frac{12}{12}$	100%	1.00
$\frac{1}{10}$		10%	0.10
$\frac{2}{10}$	$\frac{1}{5}$	20%	0.20
$\frac{3}{10}$		30%	0.30
$\frac{4}{10}$	$\frac{2}{5}$	40%	0.40
$\frac{5}{10}$	$\frac{1}{2}$ $\frac{2}{4}$ $\frac{3}{6}$ $\frac{4}{8}$ $\frac{6}{12}$	50%	0.50
$\frac{6}{10}$	$\frac{3}{5}$	60%	0.60
$\frac{7}{10}$		70%	0.70
$\frac{8}{10}$	$\frac{4}{5}$	80%	0.80
$\frac{9}{10}$		90%	0.90
$\frac{10}{10}$	$\frac{2}{2}$ $\frac{3}{3}$ $\frac{4}{4}$ $\frac{5}{5}$ $\frac{6}{6}$ $\frac{8}{8}$ $\frac{12}{12}$	100%	1.00
$\frac{1}{12}$		8.3%	0.083
$\frac{2}{12}$	$\frac{1}{6}$	16.6%	0.166
$\frac{3}{12}$	$\frac{1}{4}$ $\frac{2}{8}$	25%	0.25
$\frac{4}{12}$	$\frac{1}{3}$ $\frac{2}{6}$	33.3%	0.333
$\frac{5}{12}$		41.6%	0.416
$\frac{6}{12}$	$\frac{1}{2}$ $\frac{2}{4}$ $\frac{3}{6}$ $\frac{4}{8}$ $\frac{5}{10}$	50%	0.50
$\frac{7}{12}$		58.3%	0.583
$\frac{8}{12}$	$\frac{2}{3}$ $\frac{4}{6}$	66.6%	0.666
$\frac{9}{12}$	$\frac{3}{4}$ $\frac{6}{8}$	75%	0.75
$\frac{10}{12}$	$\frac{5}{6}$	83.3%	0.833
$\frac{11}{12}$		91.6%	0.916
$\frac{12}{12}$	$\frac{2}{2}$ $\frac{3}{3}$ $\frac{4}{4}$ $\frac{5}{5}$ $\frac{6}{6}$ $\frac{8}{8}$ $\frac{10}{10}$	100%	1.00

Geoboard Dot Paper

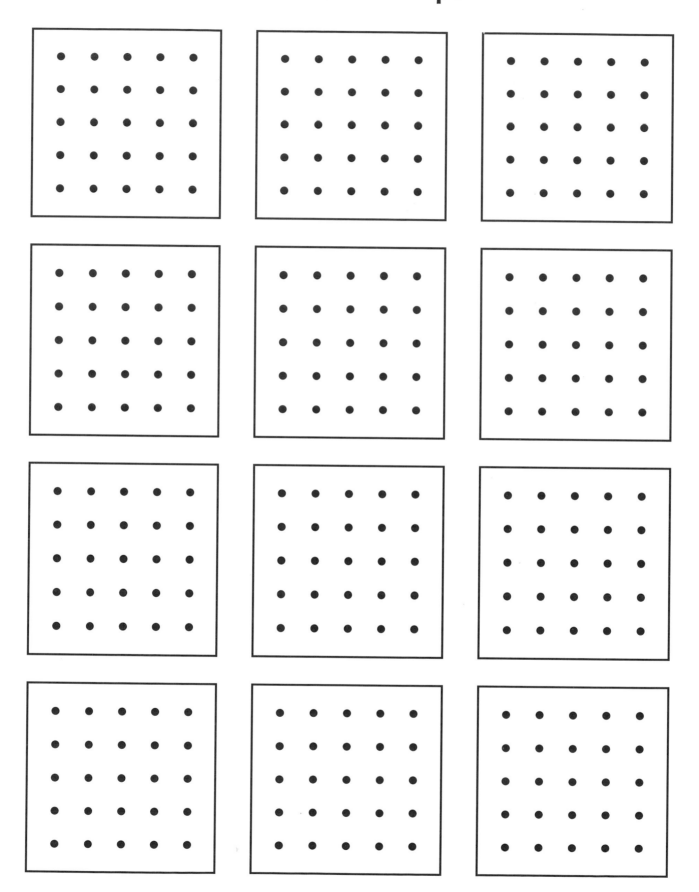

Overhead Math Discoveries, Grades 4-6
© 1993 Ideal School Supply Company

Dot Paper

How Many Numbers?

Getting Ready

- Use 1 set of Base Ten Blocks for the Overhead Projector.
- Use 1 blank transparency and a pen for the overhead projector.
- Give each pair of students a Think Sheet and a pencil.

Setting Up the Overhead Projector

- Draw the table shown on the transparency.
- Put the transparency on the projector.
- Put the Base Ten Blocks on the transparency as shown.

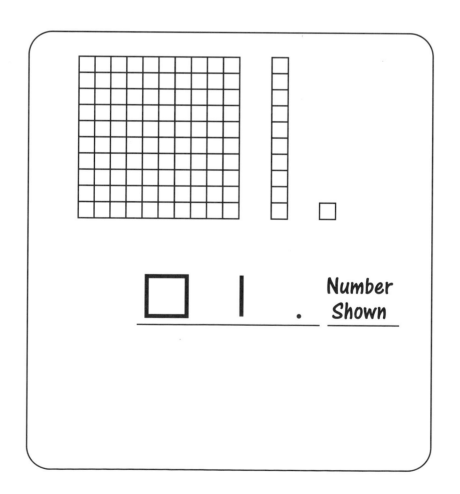

Overhead Math Discoveries, Grades 4-6
© 1993 Ideal School Supply Company

Solving Problems

Turn on the projector.

Review the value of each block with the students. Point to each block and talk about the ones-block, the tens-block, and the hundreds-block. Line up 10 ones-blocks next to the tens-block and talk about the 10 ones in ten. Then line up 10 tens-blocks under the hundreds-block to show the 10 tens in 100.

Take away all the blocks except one of each kind of block. Say: **We can show several different numbers by using just these three blocks. If we take just the hundreds-block, that shows the number 100. We can use this table to keep track of the different numbers.** Point out the symbols used for the blocks: a square for the hundreds-block, a line for the tens-block, and a dot for the ones-block. Put an **x** under the hundreds-block, and then write **100** under Number Shown.

Say: **Work with your partner and think about other numbers you can show with one or more of the blocks. Write down each number in a table like this one. I'll give you a hint: There are seven different numbers.** (100, 110, 101, 111, 10, 11, 1)

After students have had time to write their numbers, have them share their solutions. Record each answer in the table on the transparency.

Talking About Discoveries

Have students talk about how they started looking for numbers. Ask: **How did the table help you find the numbers?**

Solving More Problems

Have the students work in pairs or in groups of four. Give each group some Base Ten Blocks, paper, and pencils.

Have each group make up a How Many Numbers problem. Tell the groups to record all their solutions. Have them exchange problems with another group. Students can share their problems with the class, using the overhead projector.

Sums from Zim and Zor

Getting Ready

- Use 1 set of Base Ten Blocks for the Overhead Projector.
- Make a transparency of Sums from Zim and Zor (page 80).
- Give each group of students a Think Sheet and a pencil.

Setting Up the Overhead Projector

- Write the number on the transparency as shown.
- Put the transparency on the projector.
- Put the Base Ten Blocks on the projector as shown.

Sums for Zim and Zor

Using ___1___ block(s) from each, how many sums can you show?

Solving Problems

Turn on the projector.

Tell the students that there are several sums that can be shown by putting together one block from Zor with one block from Zim. Give an example by putting together the hundreds-block from Zim with a tens-block from Zor. Say: **Write the addition equation that this shows.** Give them time to write, and then have them share their answers. Write the addition equation: **100 + 10 = 110.**

Say: **Work together and try to think of other ways you can put together one block from Zor and one block from Zim. Write an addition equation to show each way.** After they have time to write their answers, have the groups share their solutions, and fill in the list on the transparency. (100 + 1 = 101, 10 + 10 = 20, 10 + 1 = 11, 1 + 10 = 11, 1 + 1 = 2)

Next have the students look for ways to combine any two blocks from Zor and from Zim. (110 + 20 = 130, 110 + 11 = 121, 110 + 2 = 112, 101 + 20 = 121, 101 + 11 = 112, 101 + 2 = 103, 11 + 20 = 31, 11 + 11 = 22, 11 + 2 = 13)

Finally, have the students find ways to combine any three blocks from Zor and from Zim. (111 + 30 = 141, 111 + 21 = 132, 111 + 12 = 123, 111 + 3 = 114)

Talking About Discoveries

Ask the students how they thought about combining the blocks. Did they find ways to organize their thinking. Which blocks did they begin with?

Solving More Problems

Have the students work in pairs or in groups of four. Give each group some Base Ten Blocks, a copy of Sums from Zim and Zor, and pencils.

Have the students create their own problems. Each group should record all the possible solutions. Then have groups exchange problems.

What's Left for Kron?

Getting Ready

- Use 1 set of Base Ten Blocks for the Overhead Projector.

- Make a transparency of What's Left for Kron? (page 81).

- Give each group of students a Think Sheet and a pencil.

Setting Up the Overhead Projector

- Write the number on the transparency as shown.

- Put the transparency on the projector.

- Put the Base Ten Blocks on the projector as shown.

What's Left for Kron?

How many different ways can you subtract ___1___ block(s)?

Solving Problems

Turn on the projector.

Tell the students that there are different ways to take away blocks from Kron to show subtraction equations. Take away the hundreds-block and say: **Look at what's left. Write a subtraction equation to show this.**

Give the students time to write and then ask them for their answers. Write the equation on the transparency: 124 – 100 = 24. Say: **Work together and think about other ways to take away one block. Write a subtraction equation for each way.** When the students are finished writing, have them share their solutions. (124 – 10 = 114, 124 – 1 = 123)

Next have the students look for different ways to take away two blocks from Kron. (124 – 110 = 14, 124 – 101 = 23, 124 – 20 = 104, 124 – 11 = 113, 124 – 2 = 122)

Finally, have the students find different ways to take away three blocks. (124 – 120 = 4, 124 – 111 = 13, 124 – 102 = 22, 124 – 21 = 103, 124 – 12 = 112, 124 – 3 = 121)

Talking About Discoveries

Ask the students how they thought about taking away blocks. Did they find ways to organize their thinking? How was this different from putting blocks together to show addition equations?

Solving More Problems

Have the students work in pairs or in groups of four. Give each group some Base Ten Blocks, copies of What's Left for Kron, and pencils.

Have the students create their own subtraction problems. Each group should record all the possible solutions. Then have the groups exchange their problems.

Mystery Blocks

Getting Ready

- Use 1 set of Base Ten Blocks for the Overhead Projector.

- Use a sheet of paper for covering blocks.

- Give each pair of students a Think Sheet and a pencil.

Setting Up the Overhead Projector

- Put the Base Ten Blocks on the transparency as shown.

- Cover the blocks with the sheet of paper.

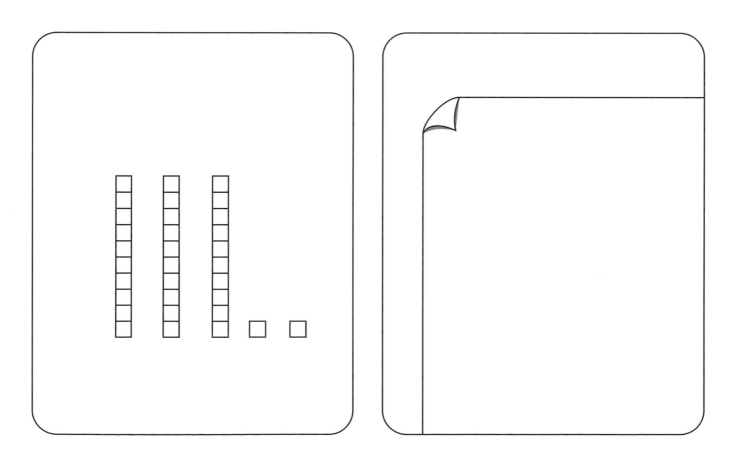

Overhead Math Discoveries, Grades 4-6
© 1993 Ideal School Supply Company

Solving Problems

Turn on the projector.

Tell the students that some mystery blocks are hidden under the sheet of paper and you are going to give them some clues to figure out what the mystery blocks are. Have the students work in pairs. Give them these clues:

A. **There are five blocks.**
   Together they show a number greater than 20.
   Together they show a number less than 50.
   Together they show an even number.

Give the students time to think about the mystery blocks and write their answers. Then uncover the blocks and let them check their solutions.

Take the blocks off the projector. Continue in the same way with these sets of mystery blocks and clues.

B. Hide these blocks: 3 tens-blocks, 3 ones-blocks.

   There are six blocks.
   Together they show a number greater than 20.
   Together they show a number less than 50.
   Together they show an odd number.

C. Hide these blocks: 1 hundreds-block, 2 tens-blocks, 2 ones-blocks.

   There are five blocks.
   Together they show a number greater than 110.
   Together they show a number less than 140.
   Together they show an even number.

Talking About Discoveries

Ask the students how they discovered the mystery blocks. What did they do first? Did they do this in their heads, or did they write down information? Did they draw groups of blocks?

Solving More Problems

Have the students work in pairs or in groups of four. Give each group some Base Ten Blocks, paper, and pencils.

Have the groups create their own Mystery Block problems. Tell each group to write down their clues. Then the groups can exchange problems.

Base Ten Palindromes

Getting Ready

- Use 1 set of Base Ten Blocks for the Overhead Projector.
- Use a blank transparency and a pen for the overhead projector.
- Give each group of students a Think Sheet and a pencil.

Setting Up the Overhead Projector

- Write the word **palindrome** and the examples on the transparency as shown.
- Put the transparency on the projector.
- Put the Base Ten Blocks on the transparency as shown.

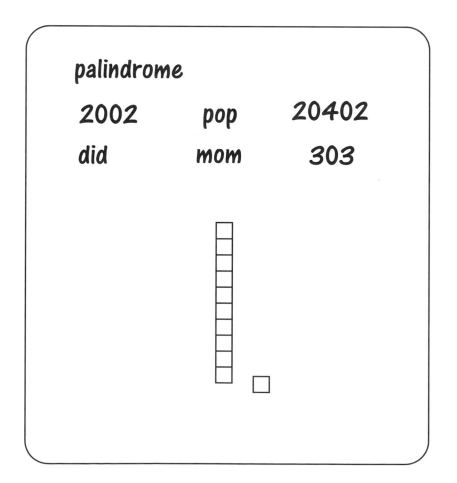

Solving Problems

Turn on the projector.

Say: **A palindrome is a number or word that reads the same backward or forward. Look at the examples.** See if anyone in the room has a name that is a palindrome and write it on the transparency.

Talk about the blocks on the projector. Talk about how the number 11 is a palindrome. Add two tens-blocks and three ones-blocks. Say: **Use one or more of these blocks and see how many palindromes you can show. Work together and write down your answers.** Give the students time to work and then have them share their answers. Write the answers on the transparency. (11, 22, 33)

Then erase any numbers written and put out a new group of blocks: one hundreds-block, three tens-blocks, three ones-blocks. Have the students try to find all the palindromes from any combination of blocks in this group. (131, 121, 101, 111, 11, 22, 33)

Talking About Discoveries

Ask the students how they found the palindromes. Did they discover helpful ways to think about this? How many numbers do they think are palindromes between 1 and 50? (4) Between 1 and 100? (9)

Solving More Problems

Have the students work in pairs or in groups of four. Give each group some Base Ten Blocks, paper, and pencils.

Have the students create their own palindrome problems. Each group should record all the possible solutions. Then groups can exchange problems and share them on the overhead projector.

The groups might also want to explore finding words that are palindromes.

Mystery Rectangles

Getting Ready

- Use 1 set of Base Ten Blocks for the Overhead Projector.

- Use a sheet of paper for covering blocks.

- Give each pair of students a Think Sheet and a pencil.

Setting Up the Overhead Projector

- Put the Base Ten Blocks on the transparency as shown.

- Cover blocks with the sheet of paper.

Solving Problems

Turn on the projector.

Ask the students to think about what multiplication problem the blocks show. (4×11) Then have them think about other ways to make a rectangle using the same blocks to show multiplcation problems. Each problem should have different numbers but the same product. (2×22, 1×44) As you get ideas from the students, rearrange the blocks. Write the different problems on the transparency.

Then say: **Under the paper are hidden a group of blocks. I'm going to give you some clues. Work together to find out what the blocks are.** Give these clues:

> **There are 12 blocks.**
> **You can make three different rectangles.**
> **The product is greater than 30 and less than 50.**
> **There are twice as many ones-blocks as tens-blocks.**

Give the students time to think about this problem. Then have them share their solutions. (4 tens-blocks, 8 ones-blocks; 1×48, 2×24, 4×12)

Take the blocks off the projector. Hide a new group of blocks and give these clues:

> **There are 15 blocks.**
> **You can make five different rectangles.**
> **The product is greater than 50 and less than 70.**
> **There are twice as many ones-blocks as tens-blocks.**

(5 tens-blocks, 10 ones-blocks; 1×60, 2×30, 3×20, 5×12, 6×10)

Talking About Discoveries

Ask the students how they found the mystery blocks. How did the clue about the product help?

Solving More Problems

Have the students work in pairs or in groups of four. Give each group some Base Ten Blocks, paper, and pencils.

Have the students create their own rectangle problems. Each group should record all the possible solutions. Then groups can exchange rectangle problems and share them on the overhead projector.

Making connections between numbers and concrete representations; exploring place value

Base Ten Numbers

Getting Ready

- Use 1 Hundred Number Board for the Overhead Projector and the blue tiles.
- Use 1 set of Base Ten Blocks for the Overhead Projector.
- Use a sheet of paper for covering blocks.
- Give each pair of students a Think Sheet and pencils.

Setting Up the Overhead Projector

- Put the Hundred Number Board on the projector.
- Put 1 tens-block and 2 ones-blocks above (or next to) the board.

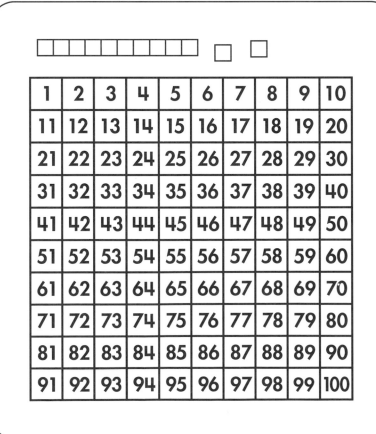

Solving Problems

Turn on the projector.

Point to the tens-block and two ones-blocks. Say: **We can show five different numbers with these blocks.** Show the numbers 1, 2, 10, 11, and 12 with the blocks, and put a blue tile on each number you show.

Take the tiles off the number board. Add one tens-block and one ones-block to the blocks above the board. Ask: **What are all the different numbers we can show with these blocks? Work with your partner. Write the numbers on your Think Sheet.** (1, 2, 3, 10, 11, 12, 13, 20, 21, 22, 23)

Give the students time to write their numbers. Then have them share their answers. Put tiles on the numbers they found. Then remove the blocks and tiles.

Say: **I am going to hide some base ten blocks under a paper, and I'll put tiles on the numbers the blocks can show. Can you figure out what blocks are under the paper? Record your answer.** Cover the space above the number board as you put out one tens-block and five ones-blocks. Keep the blocks covered. Put blue tiles on numbers 1, 2, 3, 4, 5, 10, 11, 12, 13, 14, 15.

Give the students time to record their answers. Then uncover the blocks and let them check their answers.

Continue in the same way, hiding these blocks and putting tiles on the numbers they can show.

Tens	Ones	Numbers
3	3	1, 2, 3, 10, 11, 12, 13, 20, 21, 22, 23, 30, 31, 32, 33
1	11	1, 2, 3, 4, 5, 6, 7, 8, 9, 10, 11, 12, 13, 14, 15, 16, 17, 18, 19, 20, 21

Talking About Discoveries

Ask the students how they figured out what blocks were hidden under the paper. Encourage them to talk about the different numbers that result when they use ten ones-blocks in place of a tens-block.

Solving More Problems

Have the students work together in pairs. Give each pair some Base Ten Blocks, a Hundred Number Board, and tiles for marking numbers on the number board.

Have the students take turns hiding groups of blocks and putting tiles on the number board to give clues about what blocks are hidden.

Exploring number relations; changing addends for given sums

Sums and Slides

Getting Ready

- Use 1 Hundred Number Board for the Overhead Projector, red tiles, and blue tiles.
- Give each pair of students a Think Sheet and pencils.

Setting Up the Overhead Projector

- Put the Hundred Number Board on the projector.
- Put red tiles on numbers 10 and 15. Put a blue tile on number 25.

1	2	3	4	5	6	7	8	9	10
11	12	13	14	15	16	17	18	19	20
21	22	23	24	25	26	27	28	29	30
31	32	33	34	35	36	37	38	39	40
41	42	43	44	45	46	47	48	49	50
51	52	53	54	55	56	57	58	59	60
61	62	63	64	65	66	67	68	69	70
71	72	73	74	75	76	77	78	79	80
81	82	83	84	85	86	87	88	89	90
91	92	93	94	95	96	97	98	99	100

Solving Problems

Turn on the projector.

Say: **These three numbers show an addition equation: 10 + 15 = 25. Write the equation on your Think Sheet.**

Say: **I am going to slide the red tiles to change the addends. Each time I slide the tiles, write a new addition equation. See if something curious happens!**

Slide the red tiles to each of these new positions, and give the students time to record the addition equations shown by the numbers.

A. 10 to 20	B. 20 to 17	C. 17 to 7	D. 7 to 10
15 to 5	5 to 8	8 to 18	18 to 15

Say: **Look at your equations. Did the sum change? Look at the number board and try to figure out what happened to the addends on each slide. Talk with your partner, and record your ideas.**

After the students have recorded their ideas, show this addition equation: 17 + 24 = 41. Put red tiles on numbers 17 and 24. Put a blue tile on number 41. Then make these slides:

A. 17 to 7	B. 7 to 1	C. 1 to 11	D. 11 to17
24 to 34	34 to 40	40 to 30	30 to 24

Have the partners talk together and record their ideas. Then show one more equation: 15 + 35 = 50. Make these slides.

A. 15 to 14	B. 14 to 34	C. 34 to 37	D. 37 to 7
35 to 36	36 to 16	16 to 13	13 to 43

Talking About Discoveries

Ask the students to share their discoveries about why the sum did not change. Have them tell what each slide did to the value of the addend. (Down one space adds 10; up one space subtracts10; right one space adds 1; left one space subtracts 1)

Solving More Problems

Have the students work together in pairs. Give each pair a Hundred Number Board, paper, pencils, and tiles for marking addends and sums on the number board.

Have the students write addition equations and show them with markers on the number board. Encourage them to begin with two addends, then try three addends or more.

What's My Rule?

Getting Ready

- Use 1 Hundred Number Board for the Overhead Projector; red, yellow, and blue tiles.
- Give each pair of students a Think Sheet and pencils.

Setting Up the Overhead Projector

- Put the Hundred Number Board on the projector.

1	2	3	4	5	6	7	8	9	10
11	12	13	14	15	16	17	18	19	20
21	22	23	24	25	26	27	28	29	30
31	32	33	34	35	36	37	38	39	40
41	42	43	44	45	46	47	48	49	50
51	52	53	54	55	56	57	58	59	60
61	62	63	64	65	66	67	68	69	70
71	72	73	74	75	76	77	78	79	80
81	82	83	84	85	86	87	88	89	90
91	92	93	94	95	96	97	98	99	100

Solving Problems

Turn on the projector.

Say: **I'm going to put tiles on numbers, using a rule. Watch and try to figure out my rule. Talk together and record your ideas on your Think Sheet.** Put red tiles on numbers 4, 8, 12, 16, 20, 24, 28, 32.

When the students have had time to record their ideas, ask a pair of students to tell their ideas. (The rule is: *Each number is four more than the number before it*; and/or *The numbers are multiples of 4.*)

Continue in the same way. Put red tiles on numbers 9, 18, 27, 36, 45, 54, and 63. Have the students try to find your rule and record their ideas. (The rule is: *Each number is nine more than the number before it*; and/or *The numbers are multiples of 9.*)

Continue in the same way, but say: **I am going to put tiles on pairs of numbers. The numbers in each pair are related in the same way.** Put red tiles on numbers 3 and 9; put yellow tiles on numbers 4 and 16; put blue tiles on numbers 5 and 25. (The rule is: *In each pair, one number is the square of the other number—the number multiplied by itself.*) Have the students find other number pairs on the number board that follow your rule.

Continue in the same way. Put red tiles on numbers 45 and 54; put yellow tiles on numbers 56 and 65; put blue tiles on numbers 67 and 76. (The rule is: *The second number in each pair is nine more than the first number; it's digits are the same as those in the first number, but they are reversed.*)

Talking About Discoveries

Ask the students to tell about their thinking as they tried to find your rule. Did they look for patterns? Did they count on from one number to the next when you put tiles on series of numbers?

Solving More Problems

Have the students work together in pairs. Give each pair a Hundred Number Board, tiles, paper, and pencils.

Have the students make up What's My Rule puzzles for other students to solve. Then have them present the puzzles on the overhead projector.

Number Detective

Getting Ready

- Use 1 Hundred Number Board for the Overhead Projector.
- Make a transparency of Number Detective (page 82).
- Give each pair of students a Think Sheet and pencils.

Setting Up the Overhead Projector

- Put the Hundred Number Board on the projector.
- Put the transparency over the Hundred Number Board.

1	2	3	4	5	6	7	8	9	10
11	12	13	14	15	16	17	18	19	20
21	22	23	24	25	26	27	28	29	30
31	32	33	34	35	36	37	38	39	40
41	42	43	44	45	46	47	48	49	50
51	52	53	54	55	56	57	58	59	60
61	62	63	64	65	66	67	68	69	70
71	72	73	74	75	76	77	78	79	80
81	82	83	84	85	86	87	88	89	90
91	92	93	94	95	96	97	98	99	100

Overhead Math Discoveries, Grades 4-6
© 1993 Ideal School Supply Company

Solving Problems

Turn on the projector.

Say: **I am going to give you clues about a group of mystery numbers. The nine numbers will fit in the spaces of Detective J.D.'s number detector. The clues fit every number. Jot down the clues. Write the numbers as soon as you find them.**

Move J.D.'s number detector to the side of the number board, then read these clues.

> **The ones' digit is greater than four.**
> **The tens' digit is less than seven.**
> **The difference between the digits is less than three.**
> (55, 56, 57, 65, 66, 67, 75, 76, 77)

When the students have written their mystery numbers, have one pair of students come to the projector, put the number detector on the mystery numbers, and show how each number fits the clues.

Continue in the same way, reading each of these sets of clues.

> **The ones' digit is less than five.**
> **The tens' digit is less than five.**
> **The difference between the digits is less than three.**
> (11, 12, 13, 21, 22, 23, 31, 32, 33; or 22, 23, 24, 32, 33, 34, 42, 43, 44)

> **The ones' digit is greater than six.**
> **The tens' digit is less than six.**
> **The difference between the digits is greater than one.**
> (17, 18, 19, 27, 28, 29, 37, 38, 39; or 27, 28, 29, 37, 38, 39, 47, 48, 49; or 37, 38, 39, 47, 48, 49, 57, 58, 59)

Talking About Discoveries

Ask the students to tell how they began their search each time new clues were read. Did they find any strategies for finding the group of numbers? Encourage them to show their strategies on the number board.

Solving More Problems

Have the students work together in pairs or in groups of four. Give each pair a Hundred Number Board, pencils, and paper.

Have the students write their own sets of clues about mystery numbers. Encourage them to make other shapes of "number detectors" and draw them on a blank transparency. Then have them present their Mystery Numbers puzzles to other students, using the overhead projector.

Finding differences between numbers; identifying a number pattern

Mirror Numbers

Getting Ready

- Use 1 Hundred Number Board for the Overhead Projector, and yellow tiles.

- Give each pair of students a Think Sheet and pencils.

Setting Up the Overhead Projector

- Put the Hundred Number Board on the transparency.

- Put yellow tiles on numbers 12 and 21.

1	2	3	4	5	6	7	8	9	10
11	12	13	14	15	16	17	18	19	20
21	22	23	24	25	26	27	28	29	30
31	32	33	34	35	36	37	38	39	40
41	42	43	44	45	46	47	48	49	50
51	52	53	54	55	56	57	58	59	60
61	62	63	64	65	66	67	68	69	70
71	72	73	74	75	76	77	78	79	80
81	82	83	84	85	86	87	88	89	90
91	92	93	94	95	96	97	98	99	100

Overhead Math Discoveries, Grades 4-6
© 1993 Ideal School Supply Company

Solving Problems

Turn on the projector.

Say: **Number 21 is the mirror image of number 12. Write down this pair of numbers and find the difference between them. Write your answer.**

Give the students time to record. Then say: **I am going to show more mirror number pairs. Write each pair of numbers, and find the difference between them.**

Move the tiles to the following mirror number pairs. Each time, wait and give the students time to record.

Pairs	Difference	Pairs	Difference
A. 13 and 31	9	E. 17 and 71	45
B. 14 and 41	18	F. 18 and 81	54
C. 15 and 51	27	G. 19 and 91	63
D. 16 and 61	36		

Say: **Look at the differences. Talk together about whether you see a pattern in the numbers.** Give the students time to talk. Then let them share their ideas. (The differences increase by nine.)

Say: **Here is another series of mirror number pairs. Record in the same way as you did for the first series.** Again, give the students time to record after showing each pair of numbers.

Put the yellow tiles on numbers 23 and 32, and move them as before.

Pairs	Difference	Pairs	Difference
A. 23 and 32	9	E. 27 and 72	45
B. 24 and 42	18	F. 28 and 82	54
C. 25 and 52	27	G. 29 and 92	63
D. 26 and 62	36		

Talk with the students about the patterns they noticed. Are they the same?

Talking About Discoveries

Ask the students if they think the same pattern would occur if they started with other mirror number pairs. Why or why not?

Solving More Problems

Have the students work together in pairs or in groups of four. Give each pair a Hundred Number Board, two tiles, pencils, and paper.

Have the students write clues about mirror number pairs. Tell them to give clues about the tens' digits or ones' digits, and the difference between the numbers in the pair. Have other students find the mirror number pairs.

Dr. Numo's Creatures

Getting Ready

- Use 1 Hundred Number Board for the Overhead Projector; red, yellow, and blue tiles.

- Make a transparency of Dr. Numo's Creatures (page 83).

- Give each pair of students a Think Sheet and pencils.

Setting Up the Overhead Projector

- Put the transparency on the projector.

- Put the Hundred Number Board on the transparency.

- Put a red tile on one of the creatures, and a blue tile on another creature.

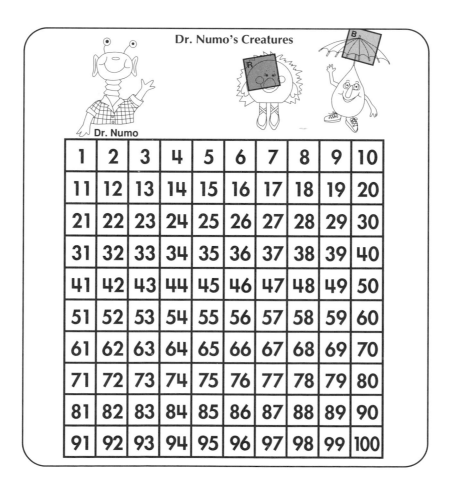

Solving Problems

Turn on the projector.

Say: **For 20 days, Dr. Numo has been watching for blue burnips and red trozzers at the water hole. A blue burnip came on these days.** Put blue tiles on numbers 4, 8, 12, 16, and 20. Say: **A red trozzer came on these days.** Put red tiles on numbers 5, 10, 15, and 20. Ask: **If Dr. Numo keeps watching for 60 days, how often will she see the red trozzer and the blue burnip at the water hole on the same day?**

Read the problem again. Then say: **Look for patterns in the numbers. Use those patterns to solve the problem.**

Give the students time to identify the patterns and extend them to find the solution. (3 times: days 20, 40, and 60.) Let a pair of students come to the projector and put red and blue tiles on the number board to show the days on which the creatures came to the water hole. Have the students describe the patterns they found and how they used them to solve the problem.

Take the tiles off the transparency and the number board. Put a yellow tile on one creature, and a blue tile on another creature. Then put blue tiles on numbers 3, 6, 9, 12, 15, 18, 21. Put yellow tiles on numbers 7, 14, and 21. Read this problem: **Dr. Numo has been watching yellow yuptoads and blue barkers come to the water hole. She has been watching for 21 days and these are the days she saw them. If she keeps watching for 60 days, how many times will she see them together?** (2 times: day 21 and day 42)

Continue in the same way as before.

Talking About Discoveries

Ask the students to tell how they found the patterns. Did any of the students make tables of numbers to help them solve the problems?

Solving More Problems

Have the students work together in pairs or groups of four. Give each pair a copy of Dr. Numo's Creatures, a Hundred Number Board, pencils, and three colors of tiles or markers.

Have the students write their own problems about Dr. Numo's creatures. Have them write problems about two or three kinds of creatures coming to the water hole. Then have them present their problems on the overhead projector for other students to solve.

Missing Fraction Pieces

Getting Ready

- Use 1 set of Fraction Builder™ Pieces for the Overhead Projector.
- Give each pair of students a Think Sheet and pencils.

Setting Up the Overhead Projector

- Put Fraction Builder pieces on the projector as shown.

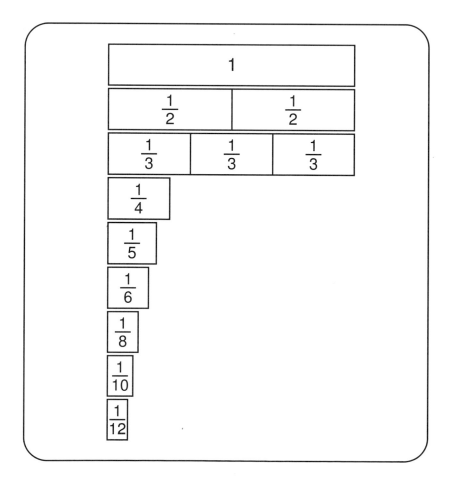

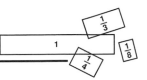

Solving Problems

Turn on the projector.

Point out the piece that represents one whole. Say: **This piece stands for one whole.**

Point out the halves and say: **Each of these pieces stands for one half, which means one of two equal pieces.**

Point out the thirds and say: **Each of these pieces stands for one third, which means one of three equal pieces.**

Say: **Look at the rest of these fraction pieces. Talk with your partner about what each piece stands for. Then make a list of the pieces that you think are missing.**

Give the students time to talk together about the missing pieces and to make a list of them. Then add the missing fourths, then the fifths, and so on until all of the pieces are on the projector. Give the students time to check their lists against the pieces shown on the projector.

Talking About Discoveries

Ask the students to tell how they figured out what pieces were missing. Did the fraction written on a piece help them figure out what pieces were missing?

Solving More Problems

Have the students work together in pairs. Give each pair a set of Fraction Builder pieces.

Have the students show fractions that require more than one piece of the same color, and write the name of each fraction with numerals and with words. For example, it they show three fourths, they would write ¾ and **three of four equal pieces.**

Hidden Fractions

Getting Ready

- Use 1 set of Fraction Builder™ Pieces for the Overhead Projector.
- Use a sheet of paper for covering fraction pieces.
- Give each pair of students a Think Sheet and pencils.

Setting Up the Overhead Projector

- Put the whole piece, one half, two fourths, and three sixths on the projector as shown.
- Cover the fourths and sixths with the paper.

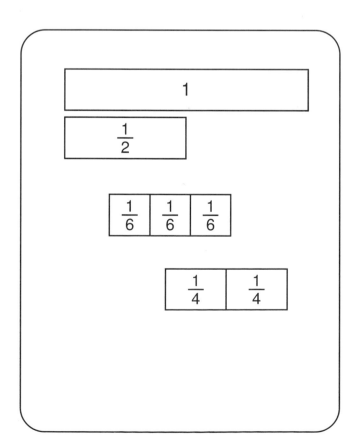
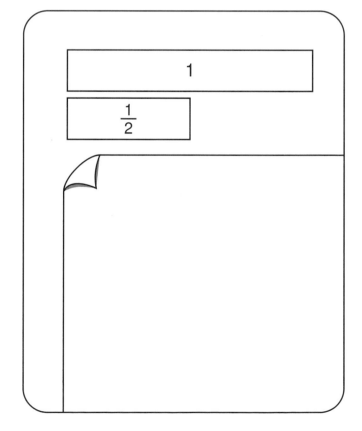

Overhead Math Discoveries, Grades 4-6
© 1993 Ideal School Supply Company

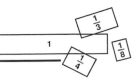

Solving Problems

Turn on the projector.

Say: **I am hiding three fraction pieces of the same color. Together they show a fraction that is equivalent to one half. What three pieces are they? Talk with your partner and write your answer on your Think Sheet.**

Give the students time to talk together about the hidden pieces and to write their answers. Then uncover the hidden sixths, and place them next to the half so that the students can check their answers.

Say: **I am hiding two fraction pieces of the same color. Together they show a fraction that is equivalent to one half. What two pieces are they? Talk with your partner and write your answer on your Think Sheet.**

Take the fourths and sixths off the projector. Cover the projector stage with the paper as you put four eighths, five tenths, and six twelfths on the projector. Keep them covered with paper. Continue as before, giving the students a clue about fraction pieces that show a fraction equivalent to one half.

You may wish to extend this activity by having the students find the fractions that are equivalent to one fourth (two eighths, three twelfths), and to one third (two sixths, four twelfths).

Talking About Discoveries

Ask the students to tell how they figured out what pieces were hidden under the paper. Did any students multiply the number of pieces you gave by 2, to find the denominator or name of the fraction pieces?

Solving More Problems

Have the students work together in pairs. Give each pair a set of Fraction Builder pieces, paper, and pencils.

Have the students write these fractions on their paper: ¼, ½, ¾, ⅓, ⅔. Have them use the Fraction Builder pieces to find as many equivalent fractions for each one as they can. Have them record the equivalent fractions, then compare their answers to those of other pairs of students.

Fraction Builder™ 3

Mystery Fractions

Getting Ready

- Use 1 set of Fraction Builder™ Pieces for the Overhead Projector.
- Give each pair of students a Think Sheet and pencils.

Setting Up the Overhead Projector

- Put Fraction Builder pieces on the transparency as shown.

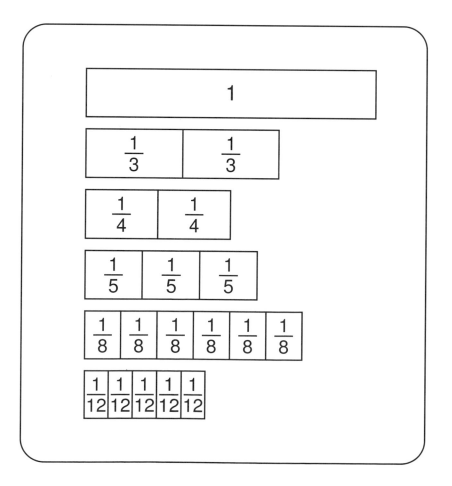

Overhead Math Discoveries, Grades 4-6
© 1993 Ideal School Supply Company

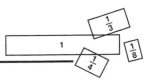

Solving Problems

Turn on the projector.

Point out the fraction pieces below the whole piece. Say: **These pieces show five fractions. I am going to give some clues about one of the fractions. See if you can identify it. Talk with your partner about it.**

> **It is greater than one half.**
> **It is equivalent to three fourths.**
> **What is it?** (six eighths)

Give the students time to talk together and identify the Mystery Fraction. Then show the students the fraction.

Continue in the same way, reading these clues:

> **It is less than three fourths.**
> **It is equivalent to the product of two times two sixths.**
> **What is it?** (two thirds)

> **It is greater than one half.**
> **It is equivalent to the sum of two tenths plus four tenths.**
> **What is it?** (three fifths)

> **It is greater than six twelfths.**
> **It is equivalent to four twelfths plus four twelfths.**
> **What is it?** (two thirds)

Talking About Discoveries

Ask the students to tell how they figured out what the Mystery Fraction was. How did they use the groups of fraction pieces to compare fractions?

Solving More Problems

Have the students work together in pairs. Give each pair a set of Fraction Builder pieces, paper, and pencils.

Have the students write their own Mystery Fraction clues and present them to the other students on the overhead projector.

Partly Percents

Getting Ready

- Use 1 set of Fraction Builder™ Pieces for the Overhead Projector.
- Make a transparency of Partly Percents (page 84).
- Give each pair of students a Think Sheet and pencils.

Setting Up the Overhead Projector

- Put the transparency on the projector.

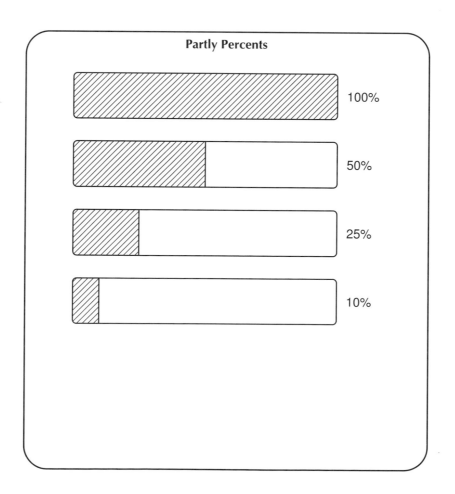

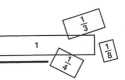

Solving Problems

Turn on the projector.

Put the whole piece on the space that represents one whole. Say: **This space represents one whole. The whole space is shaded. One whole equals one hundred percent.**

Put one half on the half-shaded space and say: **One half of this space is shaded. One half equals fifty percent.**

Ask: **What fraction piece would cover twenty-five percent of the whole? What fraction piece would cover ten percent of the whole? Write the fractions on your Think Sheet.**

Give the students time to write the fractions. Then put one fourth on the 25% space, and one tenth on the 10% space.

Take the fraction pieces off. Then say: **I'm going to show fractions with fraction pieces. Each fraction I show will cover one of the shaded areas. Write each fraction as I show it, and write what percent it is of one whole.** Show each of the following fractions, putting the pieces at the bottom of the projector stage. Each time, give the students time to write the percent, then put the fraction pieces on the equivalent shaded area.

Fractions	Solutions	Fractions	Solutions
$^5/_{10}$	50%	$^2/_4$	50%
$^6/_6$	100%	$^3/_{12}$	25%
$^1/_{10}$	10%	$^4/_8$	50%
$^6/_{12}$	50%	$^2/_8$	25%

Talking About Discoveries

Ask the students to tell how they figured out what percent of the whole would be covered by each fraction.

Solving More Problems

Have the students work together in pairs. Give each pair a set of Fraction Builder pieces, a paper copy of Partly Percents, and pencils.

Have the students find all of the fractions that are equivalent to the percents shown. Encourage them to show other fractions that are equivalent to other percents, such as three fourths.

Money Mix

Getting Ready

- Use 1 set of Fraction Builder™ Pieces for the Overhead Projector.

- Make a transparency of Money Mix (page 85), and cut apart the strips.

- Divide the students into groups of four. Give each group one or more of the transparency strips, Think Sheets, and pencils.

Setting Up the Overhead Projector

- Put the whole, one fourth, and one tenth pieces on the projector.

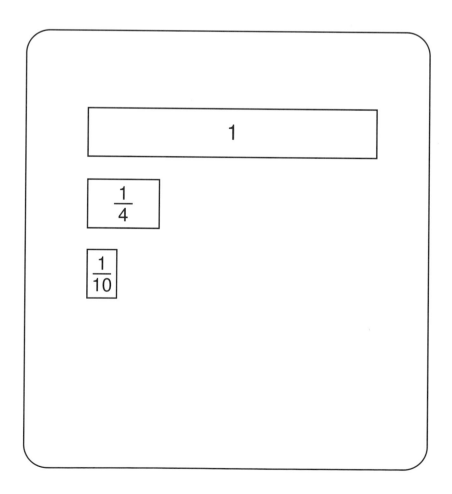

Overhead Math Discoveries, Grades 4-6
© 1993 Ideal School Supply Company

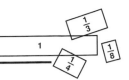

Solving Problems

Turn on the projector.

Point out the whole piece and say: **This piece represents one dollar. One whole is equivalent to one hundred cents.**

Put the fourth on or next to the whole piece and say: **One fourth is equivalent to one quarter, or twenty-five cents.** Take the fourth away and put one tenth on or next to the whole piece. Say: **One tenth is equivalent to one dime, or ten cents.** Take the tenth off the projector.

Say: **Look at the amount of money shown on your transparent strip. Some strips give exact amounts of money, but others give approximate amounts; for example,** *about thirty-three cents.* **I am going to show fractions with fraction pieces. If the fraction I show is equivalent to your amount of money, record it on your Think Sheet.**

Show the following fractions, using fraction pieces. Place the fraction pieces on or next to the whole piece. (Each column includes all of the fractions equivalent to the money amounts on the transparency strips.)

Fractions	Solutions	Fractions	Solutions
$^6/_{10}$	$0.60	$^9/_{12}$	$0.75
$^3/_4$	$0.75	$^5/_{10}$	$0.50
$^1/_2$	$0.50	$^2/_6$	about $0.33
$^3/_4$	$0.75	$^2/_{10}$	$0.20
$^1/_5$	$0.20	$^2/_5$	$0.40
$^4/_{10}$	$0.40	$^3/_5$	$0.60
$^4/_5$	$0.80	$^8/_{10}$	$0.80
$^1/_3$	about $0.33	$^2/_3$	about $0.67
$^4/_6$	about $0.67	$^1/_6$	about $0.17
$^2/_{12}$	about $0.17	$^2/_8$	$0.25

When you have finished, let a pair of students from each group bring their transparency strip to the projector and use fraction pieces to show one fraction equivalent to their money amount.

Talking About Discoveries

Ask the students to tell how they figured out what fractions would be equivalent to their money amount.

Solving More Problems

Have the students work together in pairs. Give each pair a set of Fraction Builder pieces, a paper copy of Money Mix, and pencils.

Have the students find all of the fractions they can show that are equivalent to the amounts of money given.

Fraction Bingo

Getting Ready

- Use 1 set of Fraction Builder™ Pieces for the Overhead Projector.

- Use a blank transparency and a pen for the overhead projector.

- Give each student a Think Sheet and a pencil.

Setting Up the Overhead Projector

- Write the list of percents and decimals on the transparency as shown. Draw a four-by-four grid on the transparency.

- Put the transparency on the projector.

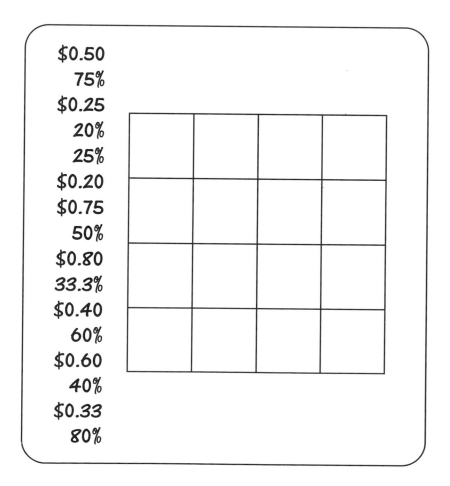

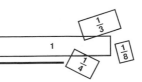

Solving Problems

Turn on the projector.

Have the students draw the grid on their Think Sheets. Then have them write the percents and decimals in any order in the spaces of their grid.

When the students have completed their Bingo boards, say: **I am going to show fractions with fraction pieces. When I show a fraction that is equivalent to a number on your Bingo board, write the fraction in the space with the number. You may write the fraction in only one space. As soon as you have written fractions in four connected spaces—in any direction—say "Bingo."**

Show the following fractions in any order, using the fraction pieces. Let students find equivalent numbers on their boards.

Fractions	Decimals, Percents	Fractions	Decimals, Percents
$^5/_{10}$	$0.50, 50%	$^2/_4$	$0.50, 50%
$^3/_4$	$0.75, 75%	$^2/_{10}$	$0.20, 20%
$^3/_{12}$	$0.25, 25%	$^6/_8$	$0.75, 75%
$^1/_5$	$0.20, 20%	$^1/_4$	$0.25, 25%
$^6/_{10}$	$0.60, 60%	$^8/_{10}$	$0.80, 80%
$^4/_5$	$0.80, 80%	$^3/_5$	$0.60, 60%
$^1/_3$	$0.33, 33.3%	$^2/_6$	$0.33, 33.3%
$^4/_{10}$	$0.40, 40%	$^2/_5$	$0.40, 40%

Talking About Discoveries

Ask the students to describe how they matched each fraction with an equivalent percent or decimal number. What was their thinking as they tried to find equivalent numbers?

Solving More Problems

Have the students work together in pairs. Give each pair a set of Fraction Builder pieces, paper, and pencils.

Have the students make a list of eight fractions they can show with the fraction pieces. Then have them make their own Bingo boards, using equivalent decimals and percents for those fractions. (You may want to encourage them to use a calculator for fractions having the number 3, 6, or 12 as its denominator. Tell them to round the decimals to the nearest penny.) Let them use the overhead projector to present their Bingo game to other students.

All About Tangrams

Getting Ready

- Use 1 set of Tangrams for the Overhead Projector.
- Use 1 blank transparency and a pen for the overhead projector.
- Give each group of students a Think Sheet and a pencil.

Setting Up the Overhead Projector

- Draw a circle on the transparency as shown.
- Put the transparency on the projector.
- Put the tangram pieces on the transparency as shown.

Overhead Math Discoveries, Grades 4-6
© 1993 Ideal School Supply Company

Solving Problems

Turn on the projector.

Tell the students that this is a set of tangram pieces. Say: **Look at the pieces carefully. Think about how they are alike and how they are different. First we're going to sort the pieces by the number of sides they have. Look at the tangrams and think about which pieces have three sides. Work together and record which pieces you think belong in the circle.**

Give the students time to record. Get their responses, then put all five triangles in the circle. Say: **All five of these triangles have three sides. Are they alike in other ways? How are they different?** Have the students share their ideas.

Take the triangles out of the circle and continue in the same way with these questions: **Which tangram pieces have sides that are all the same length?** (square) **How many pieces have right angles?** (four triangles, square) **How many pieces have all right angles?** (square) **How many pieces do not have any right angles?** (parallelogram)

Play Mystery Tangrams. Give the students a set of clues. See if they can guess the mystery piece. Here is an example:

> **I have three sides.**
> **I am the only piece this size and shape.**
> **Who am I?** (medium triangle)

Talking About Discoveries

Ask the students what they discovered about how the tangram pieces are alike and different? Ask them whether they think they could put some pieces together to make other shapes.

Solving More Problems

Have the students work in pairs or in groups of four. Give each group a set of tangrams, paper, and pencils.

Have the groups play the Mystery Tangram game. Have students take turns making up clues that describe one tangram piece. Have groups share their Mystery Tangram clues, using the overhead projector.

Cutting Up Tangrams

Getting Ready

- Use 1 set of Tangrams for the Overhead Projector.

- Make a transparency of Cutting Up Tangrams (page 86).

- Give each student 4-inch-by-4-inch pieces of paper and scissors.

Setting Up the Overhead Projector

- Put the Cutting Up Tangrams transparency on the projector.

- Put the tangram pieces on top of the tangram square, matching the pieces to the outline on the square.

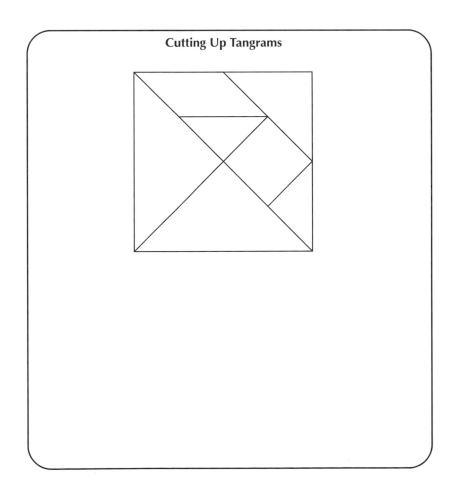

Cutting Up Tangrams

Solving Problems

Turn on the projector.

Talk about the square made up of tangrams. Say: **Your square is exactly the same size as the square on the projector. Think about how you could fold your square so that you could cut it into the seven tangram pieces. Look carefully at the way the pieces fit together on the projector. Share ideas with your partner and then try folding and cutting. If one piece doesn't work out right, just try folding and cutting another square.**

If students are having trouble with this, you can help by giving some ideas for folding their squares. Here is a step-by-step illustration of one way to fold and cut the square into the seven pieces. The shaded numbered shapes show the seven tangram pieces.

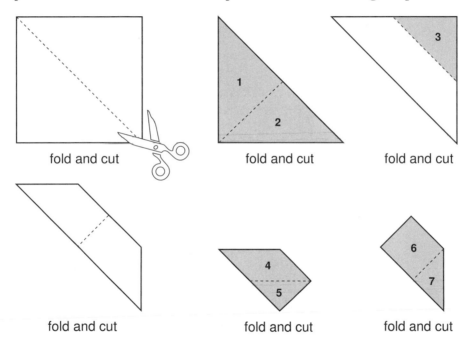

fold and cut

fold and cut

fold and cut

fold and cut

fold and cut

fold and cut

Talking About Discoveries

Ask: **What did you discover as you folded your square? Did anything surprising happen? What did you discover about the shapes of the pieces?**

Solving More Problems

Have the students work together in pairs.

Have the children explore putting their paper tangram pieces together to make a square. Have them try covering one piece with other pieces, and putting pieces together to make other shapes.

Tangram Memory Game

Getting Ready

- Use 4 sets of Tangrams for the Overhead Projector.

- Use a sheet of paper for covering the shapes.

- Give each student a Think Sheet and a pencil.

Setting Up the Overhead Projector

- Make shapes on the projector as shown.

- Cover the shapes with the sheet of paper.

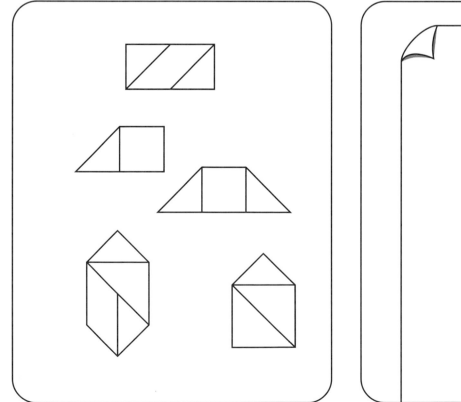

Overhead Math Discoveries, Grades 4-6
© 1993 Ideal School Supply Company

Solving Problems

Turn on the projector.

Tell the students that there are different shapes made with tangram pieces under the paper. Say: **I'm going to uncover one shape for a couple of seconds, then cover it again. Look at the shape carefully when I uncover it, then try to draw the shape on your paper.**

Uncover the rectangle long enough for the students to get a mental image of it, but not long enough for them to draw it. Then cover it and give the students time to draw it. After the students have finished drawing the shape, uncover it and let them compare their drawings to the shape on the projector.

Continue with the other shapes in the same way.

When the students have drawn all five shapes, have them label each one. (rectangle, trapezoids, pentagon, hexagon)

Talking About Discoveries

Ask the students what they did to help them remember each shape. What did they think about when they looked at a shape on the screen?

Solving More Problems

Have the students work together in pairs. Give each pair a set of tangrams, paper, and pencils.

Have the students try putting the pieces together to make shapes that are the same as the ones you showed. Have them try to use as many pieces as possible to make a rectangle, trapezoid, pentagon, and hexagon.

Tangram Parallelograms

Getting Ready

- Use 4 sets of Tangrams for the Overhead Projector.
- Make paper copies of Cutting Up Tangrams (page 86).
- Use a sheet of paper for covering pieces.
- Give each pair of students a copy of Cutting Up Tangrams and scissors. Have them cut out a set of tangrams.

Setting Up the Overhead Projector

- Put the tangram pieces on the projector as shown.
- Cover the shapes with the sheet of paper.

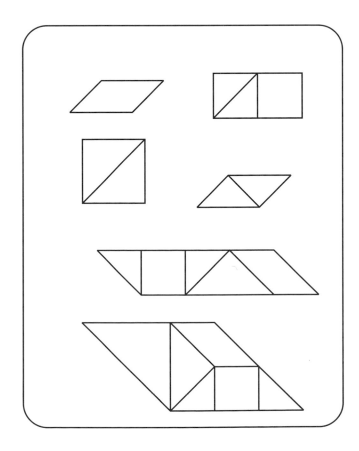

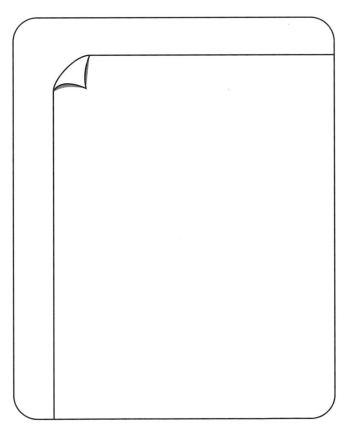

Solving Problems

Turn on the projector.

Review the definition of parallelograms with your students: *Two pairs of opposite sides are parallel and two pairs of opposite sides have the same length.* Point out how the tangram parallelogram fits the definition.

Then say: **Underneath the paper are more parallelograms made with different numbers of tangram pieces. I'm going to uncover them one at a time. Look carefully, then when I cover a shape, try making the same shape with your tangram pieces.**

First uncover the parallelogram made with two tangram pieces. Uncover the shape long enough for the students to get a mental image of it, but not long enough for them to make it. Then cover it and tell the students to make a parallelogram like this using two of their tangram pieces. Give them time to make their shape, then uncover it so they can compare their shapes to the one on the projector.

Continue to uncover the other parallelograms, telling the students how many tangram pieces to use when constructing their own shapes.

Talking About Discoveries

Talk about what students discovered about parallelograms when they made their shapes. How are they alike and how are they different? Ask them to share what helped them remember the shapes on the projector.

Solving More Problems

Have the students work in pairs. Give each pair a set of tangrams, paper, and pencils.

Have the students explore making trapezoids with different numbers of tangram pieces. Have them record their shapes on paper. Then have the pairs share their solutions on the overhead projector.

Tangram Puzzlers

Getting Ready

- Use 4 sets of Tangrams for the Overhead Projector.

- Make paper copies of Cutting Up Tangrams (page 86).

- Give each pair of students a copy of Cutting Up Tangrams and scissors. Have them cut out a set of tangrams.

Setting Up the Overhead Projector

- Make the trapezoid with tangram pieces as shown.

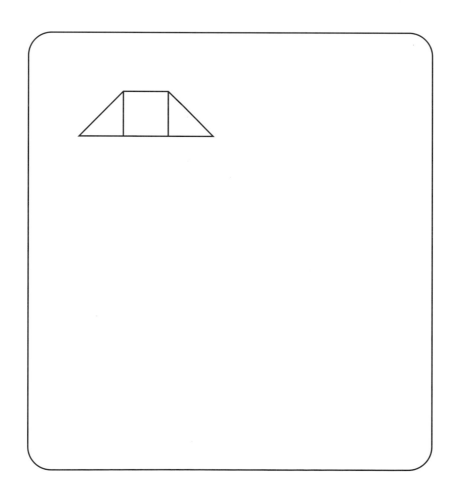

Solving Problems

Turn on the projector.

Have the students use their tangram pieces to make the trapezoid. Then say: **By moving only one piece of your trapezoid, you can make a rectangle.** Give them time to explore which piece to move, then have a student demonstrate the move on the projector. Then say: **By moving only one piece of the rectangle, it is possible to make a parallelogram that has no right angles.** As before, give them time to explore which piece to move, then have a student demonstrate the move on the projector. Then say: **By moving only one piece of the parallelogram, you can make a triangle.** Repeat the follow-up as before.

Take the square off the projector. Add the medium triangle and make this rectangle:

Now tell the students that by moving only one piece they can make a triangle, a parallelogram that has no right angles, and a trapezoid. Have them experiment and then show their solutions using the projector.

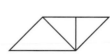

Talking About Discoveries

Ask students what they discovered about changing shapes when they moved one piece. Could they make any other shapes?

Solving More Problems

Have the students work in pairs. Give each pair a set of tangrams, paper, and pencils.

Have the students experiment with creating their own tangram puzzlers. Have them record their solutions. Then have pairs exchange puzzlers. Let some of the pairs share their puzzlers, using the overhead projector.

Angle Puzzles

Getting Ready

- Use 1 set of Tangrams for the Overhead Projector.

- Make a transparency and paper copies of Angle Puzzles (page 87).

- Make paper copies of Cutting Up Tangrams (page 86).

- Give each pair of students a copy of Angle Puzzles, Cutting Up Tangrams and scissors. Have the students cut out the tangrams.

Setting Up the Overhead Projector

- Put the transparency on the projector.

- Put the tangram pieces on the transparency as shown.

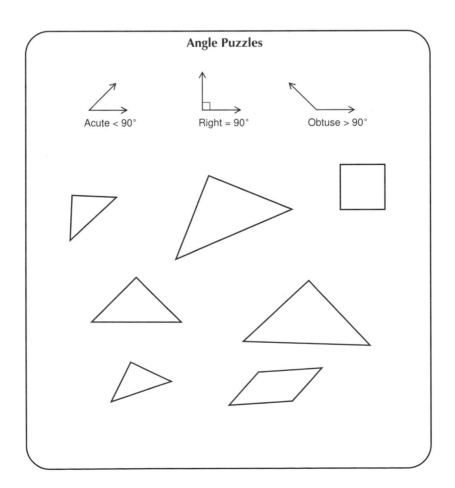

Solving Problems

Turn on the projector.

Talk about the different angles that are shown on the transparency. Put the corners of the small triangle next to each angle on the transparency. Show the right angle, the two acute angles, and how the small triangle's corners compare to the obtuse angle. Then say: **Look at the corners of each tangram piece. Talk together and decide if each corner is a right angle, acute angle, or obtuse angle. How many angles do you find of each kind? Record your answers.**

Give the students time to explore the angles of the tangram set. Then have them share their findings. (23 angles: 9 right, 12 acute, 2 obtuse)

Give the students the following problems to explore, using their tangram pieces:

1. Use 1 parallelogram, 1 medium triangle, and 1 small triangle. Make a shape having 3 right angles, 0 acute angles, and 2 obtuse angles.

2. Use 1 parallelogram, 1 large triangle, and 1 small triangle. Make a shape having 1 right angle, 1 acute angle, and 3 obtuse angles.

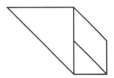

Talking About Discoveries

Ask students what they discovered about the angles of the tangrams. Do they think they could make a shape having all obtuse angles?

Solving More Problems

Have the students work in pairs. Give each pair a set of tangrams, paper, and pencils.

Have each pair explore making Angle Puzzles. Have them write which pieces to use, the number, and kinds of angles for each shape. Have pairs exchange puzzles and share them on the overhead projector.

Shapes Under Cover

Getting Ready

- Use 1 Geoboard for the Overhead Projector; small and medium rubber bands.
- Use a half-sheet of paper for covering shapes.
- Give each student a copy of geoboard dot paper (page 6) and a pencil.

Setting Up the Overhead Projector

- Make the shapes on the geoboard as shown.
- Put the geoboard on the projector.
- Cover the shapes with the paper.

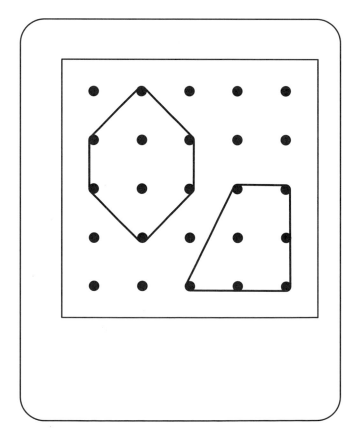

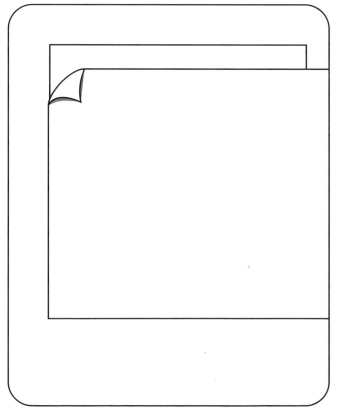

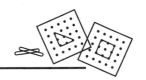

Solving Problems

Turn on the projector.

Say: **There are shapes hidden under this paper. I am going to uncover each shape for a few seconds, then cover it again and have you draw it on your dot paper.**

Uncover the hexagon long enough for the students to get a good visual image of it, but not long enough for them to draw it. Then cover it and give the students time to draw it. After the students have finished drawing the shape, uncover it and let them compare their drawings to the shape on the geoboard.

Then continue in the same way with the trapezoid.

Make any of the shapes shown below and continue in the same way.

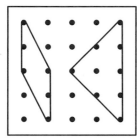 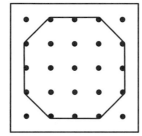 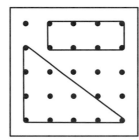 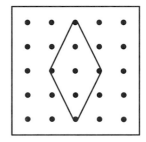

Talking About Discoveries

Ask the students what helped them remember the shapes when you covered them. Did they keep a picture of the shapes in their minds? Did they picture the pins of the geoboard? Did they count the sides?

Solving More Problems

Have the students work together in pairs or in groups of four. Give each group a geoboard, rubber bands, geoboard dot paper, a half-sheet of paper for covering shapes, and pencils.

Have the students take turns making shapes on the geoboard and drawing the shapes on dot paper. One student can make a shape on the geoboard, then show it for a few seconds, then cover it while the other students draw the shape from memory.

Stretch or Shrink

Getting Ready

- Use 1 Geoboard for the Overhead Projector; small and medium rubber bands.
- Give each student a copy of geoboard dot paper (page 6) and a pencil.

Setting Up the Overhead Projector

- Make the shapes on the geoboard as shown.
- Put the geoboard on the projector.

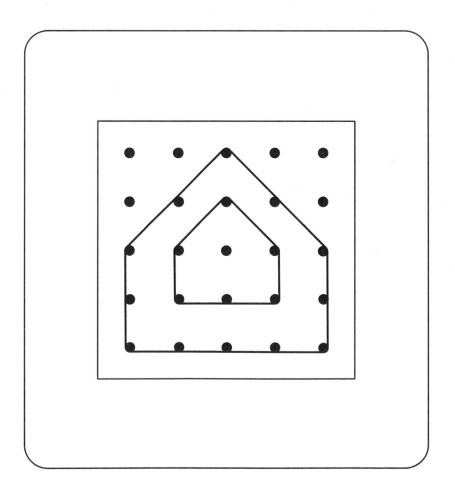

Solving Problems

Turn on the projector.

Say: **These are similar shapes. They are not the same size, but they are the same shape.** Point to the left side of the large pentagon, then to the corresponding side of the small pentagon. Say: **Think about how these sides compare.** Point to each of the other corresponding sides of the pentagons, each time asking the students to compare them. Then have one pair of students come to the projector and describe how all the corresponding sides compare. (Each side of the large pentagon is two times the length of the corresponding side in the small pentagon.)

Now point to one of the right angles in the large pentagon, then to the corresponding angle of the small pentagon. Say: **Think about how these angles compare.** Continue in the same way as you did with the sides. (The corresponding angles are exactly the same.)

Say: **I am going to make some shapes on the geoboard. As I make a shape, draw it on one of your dot grids. Then think how you could stretch or shrink the sides to make a similar shape. Remember that if you make one side twice as long, you have to make every side twice as long. Keep corresponding angles the same. Draw the similar shape.**

(The shape is shown by a solid line, the similar shape by a dotted line.)

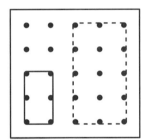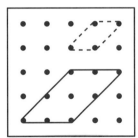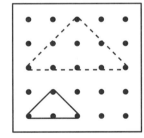

Talking About Discoveries

Ask the students what they discovered about the sides and angles of similar shapes.

Solving More Problems

Have the students work together in pairs or in groups of four. Give each group a geoboard, rubber bands, dot paper (page 7), and pencils.

Have the students make similar shapes on the geoboard. Tell them to try making similar parallelograms, trapezoids, hexagons, and pentagons. Have them draw the similar shapes on dot paper, then draw even larger ones.

Spacey Shapes

Getting Ready

- Use 1 Geoboard for the Overhead Projector; small and medium rubber bands.
- Make a transparency of Spacey Shapes (page 88).
- Use a pen for the overhead projector.
- Give each pair of students a copy of geoboard dot paper (page 6) and a pencil.

Setting Up the Overhead Projector

- Put the transparency on the projector.
- Put the geoboard on the transparency and make the square as shown.

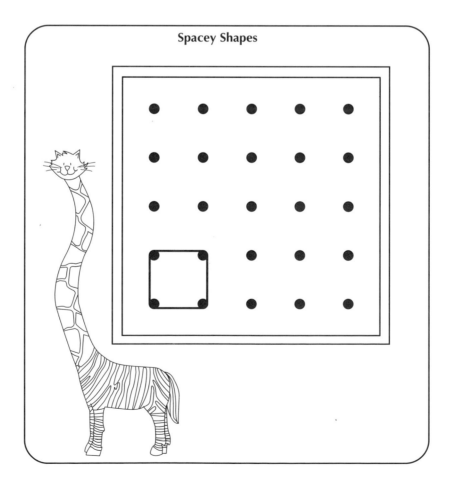

Spacey Shapes

Solving Problems

Turn on the projector.

Point to one side of the square and say: **Let's say that each side of this square is one unit long. The perimeter of the square, or distance around the edge, is four units.** Point out the area inside the square and say: **The space inside this square is one square unit of area.**

Say: **I'm going to make some shapes on the geoboard. Draw each shape on your dot paper. Record the perimeter and area of each shape.** Tell the students to draw the first shape and write **P = 4** and **A = 1** inside the shape.

Make each of these shapes and let the students draw them and record the perimeter and area.

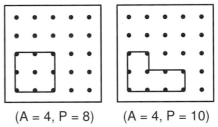

(A = 4, P = 8)   (A = 4, P = 10)

When you have finished making the shapes and the students have finished recording, give them the measures of the area and perimeters.

Then ask: **Can you make shapes with 4, 5, 6, 7, and 8 square units of area, but all having perimeters 12 units long? Work with your partner. Draw the shapes on your dot paper.** (Solutions shown below.)

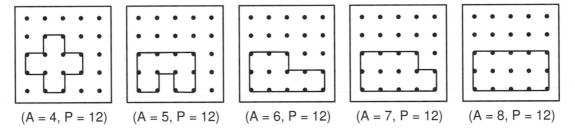

(A = 4, P = 12)   (A = 5, P = 12)   (A = 6, P = 12)   (A = 7, P = 12)   (A = 8, P = 12)

Talking About Discoveries

Ask the students how they worked to solve the problem. Did they find an organized way to find the solutions? What did they find out about the area and perimeter of shapes?

Solving More Problems

Have the students work together in pairs or in groups of four. Give each group a geoboard, rubber bands, geoboard dot paper, and pencils.

Have the students make shapes on the geoboard and draw the shapes on dot paper. Have them record the perimeter and area of each shape. Then have them cut apart their dot grids and group the shapes by area or by perimeter. They may want to display the shapes on a bulletin board and describe what they discovered about the perimeter and area of shapes.

We Half to Find the Area

Getting Ready

- Use 1 Geoboard for the Overhead Projector; small and medium rubber bands.

- Use a pen for the overhead projector.

- Give each student a copy of geoboard dot paper (page 6) and a pencil.

Setting Up the Overhead Projector

- Put the geoboard on the transparency and make the square as shown, using double rubber bands.

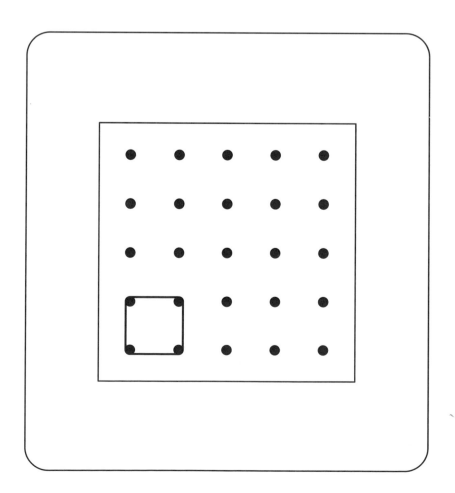

Solving Problems

Turn on the projector.

Point to one of the sides of the square. Say: **Let's say that each side of this square is one unit long.** Point out the area inside the square. Say: **The space inside this square is one square unit of area.**

Now move one of the rubber bands so that it divides the square into two equal triangles. Ask: **If the area of the square is one square unit, what is the area of each of these triangles?** (One-half square unit)

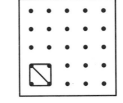

Make each of these rectangles on the geoboard, using double rubber bands. Have the students record the area of the rectangle. Then move one of the rubber bands to divide the rectangle into equal triangles. Have the students record the area of each triangle.

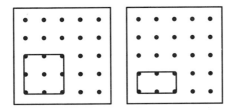

Then say: **Try to draw triangles that have areas equal to two, three, four, and six square units.** (Solutions shown below.)

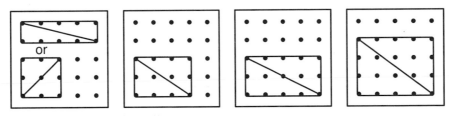

Talking About Discoveries

Ask the students how they solved the problems. How did they get started after they knew the area of a triangle?

Solving More Problems

Have the students work together in pairs or in groups of four. Give each group a geoboard, rubber bands, dot paper (page 7), and pencils.

Have the students take turns making rectangles on the geoboard and drawing the shapes on dot paper. Tell them to use double rubber bands to make each rectangle. Have them divide the rectangle into two equal triangles. Have them draw the rectangle and record the areas of the rectangle and each triangle.

Take a Turn

Getting Ready

- Use 1 Geoboard for the Overhead Projector; small and medium rubber bands.
- Make a transparency of Take a Turn (page 89).
- Give each student a sheet of geoboard dot paper (page 6) and a pencil.

Setting Up the Overhead Projector

- Put the transparency on the projector and tape the corners down.
- Put a piece of tape on one corner of the geoboard.
- Make the shape on the geoboard, as shown, and put the geoboard on the transparency.

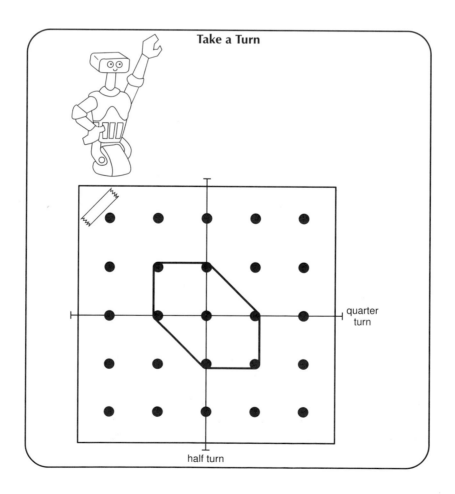

Take a Turn

quarter turn

half turn

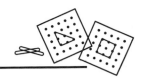

Solving Problems

Turn on the projector.

Tell the students to look at the shape on the geoboard and to draw it on their dot paper exactly as they see it. After they have drawn it, say: **Now imagine what the shape will look like when we turn it a quarter of the way around the circle, going clockwise. Draw what you think the shape will look like then.**

When the students have finished drawing, turn the geoboard clockwise, keeping the center pin on the dot. Turn the geoboard until the tape is in the upper right-hand corner. Let the students compare their drawing to the shape as it looks now.

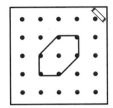

Then say: **Imagine what the shape will look like when we turn it another quarter of the way, to the half-turn mark. Draw what you think it will look like then.**

When the students have finished drawing, turn the geoboard until the tape is in the bottom right-hand corner. Let the students compare their drawings to the shape as it looks now.

Continue in the same way, turning the shape another quarter-turn, then back to its original position.

Continue this activity, making and turning any of the shapes below.

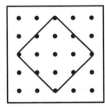 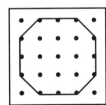 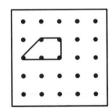 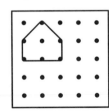 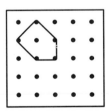

Talking About Discoveries

Ask: **How did you imagine a shape turning? Did you use the pins on the geoboard or dots on dot paper? What shapes looked the same after one turn, two turns, or every turn? Why do you think that was so?**

Solving More Problems

Have the students work together in pairs or in groups of four. Give each pair a geoboard, rubber bands, geoboard dot paper, and pencils.

Have the students make shapes and draw them in one position, then draw them again after a quarter turn, after a half turn, and after three quarter turns. Tell them to draw the shape all four times on the same dot grid and see what design results.

Changing side lengths in squares and triangles; identifying and extending number patterns

Growing on Geoboards

Getting Ready

- Use 1 Geoboard for the Overhead Projector; small and medium rubber bands.

- Use a blank transparency and a pen for the overhead projector.

- Give each pair of students a Think Sheet, dot paper (page 7), and pencils.

Setting Up the Overhead Projector

- Write the headings of the table on the transparency as shown.

- Put the transparency on the projector.

- Make the square on the geoboard, as shown, and put the geoboard on the transparency.

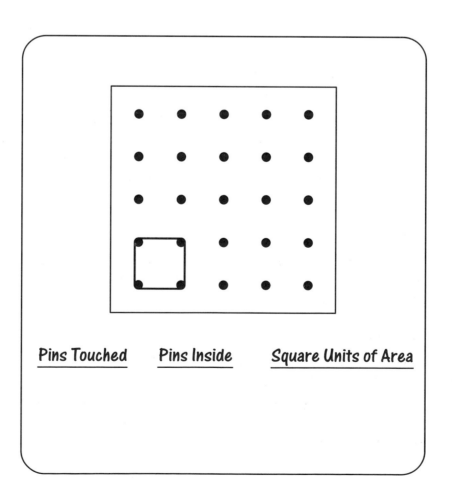

Pins Touched   Pins Inside   Square Units of Area

Overhead Math Discoveries, Grades 4-6
© 1993 Ideal School Supply Company

Solving Problems

Turn on the projector.

Tell the students to copy the headings of the table on their Think Sheets. After they have finished, say: **I am going to show you some squares. Record the number of pins touched by the square, the number of pins inside the square, and the number of square units of area inside each square.**

Make this sequence of squares on the geoboard:

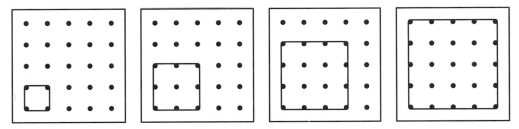

Have one pair of students fill in the numbers in the table on the transparency. Then say: **Our geoboard is too small to make the next square. Can you predict what the numbers would be for it? Look for a pattern in the numbers. Talk together and write your prediction.** (The table is shown below, with a discussion of the pattern.)

Pins Touched	Pins Inside	Square Units of Area
4	0	1
8	1	4
12	4	9
16	9	16
20	16	25

(The number of pins touched increases by 4 each time. The number of pins inside increases by 1, then 3, then 5, then 7, and so on. The number of square units of area increases by 3, then 5, then 7, then 9, and so on.)

Have a student explain the pattern. Then have the students draw the next two squares in the sequence on their dot paper. Record in the table.

Talking About Discoveries

Ask: **How did you find the patterns in the numbers?**

Solving More Problems

Have the students work together in pairs or in groups of four. Give each pair a geoboard, rubber bands, dot paper (page 7), and pencils.

Have the students make a sequence of triangles and record in a table. Have them find the patterns in the numbers, predict the numbers for the next-size triangle, then draw it to check.

What Are Attribute Blocks?

Getting Ready

- Use 1 set of Attribute Blocks for the Overhead Projector.
- Use a bag or box with a lid for hiding blocks.
- Give each group of students a Think Sheet and a pencil.

Setting Up the Overhead Projector

- Put the Attribute Blocks on the projector as shown.
- Put the rest of the blocks in a bag or box.

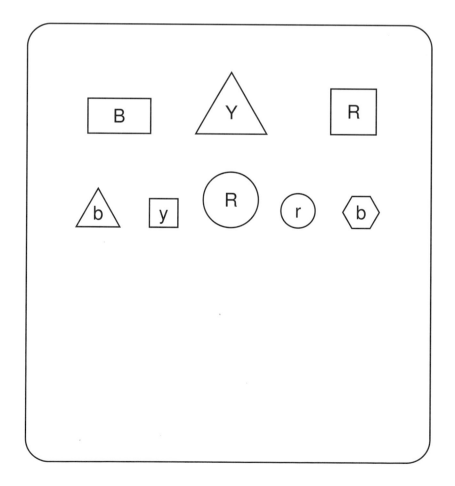

Solving Problems

Turn on the projector.

Say: **These blocks are part of a set of 30 blocks. We call them Attribute Blocks. The rest of the blocks are in this bag.** Rattle the bag so they can hear the blocks. **Look carefully at the eight blocks on the projector. See if you can tell about one of the blocks in this bag.** When you get a correct response, take that block out of the bag and display it on the projector. After a few more blocks are added to the projector, say: **Look at all these blocks. Talk in your groups and see if you can make a list of all 30 blocks in the set.**

Give the students time to make their lists. If they are having trouble, give them more hints. For example: There are 15 large blocks in the set. When the students are finished making their lists, have one group suggest two or three more blocks that they think are in the set. If they are right, add these blocks to the ones on the projector. Let other groups give their ideas for two or three blocks.

Be sure to talk about the attributes of the set: color, shape, and size. Also have the students help you make a list of the values for each attribute. For color: red, yellow, blue; for shape: circle, square, triangle, hexagon, rectangle; for size: large, small.

Talk about the symbols students can use to record the Attribute Blocks on their Think Sheets:

Shapes: □ ⬡ ◯ ▭ △

Color and Size: Y = large yellow   y = small yellow
                 B = large blue   b = small blue
                 R = large red   r = small red

Example: (B) = large blue circle

Talking About Discoveries

Ask each group how they made their list. What clues helped them? Did they organize their information in any way? Which blocks did they miss?

Solving More Problems

Have the students work in pairs or in groups of four. Give each group a set of Attribute Blocks. If the students are using a 60-piece set of Attribute Blocks, discuss the attribute of thickness.

Have the students take any block. Then tell them to look for blocks that they think are different in one way from that block. They can also look for blocks that are different in two ways or three ways.

Attribute Towers

Getting Ready

- Use 1 set of Attribute Blocks for the Overhead Projector.
- Give each group of students a Think Sheet and a pencil.

Setting Up the Overhead Projector

- Put the Attribute Blocks on the projector as shown.

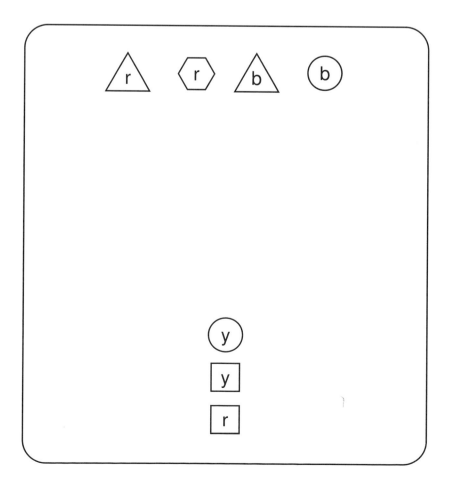

Solving Problems

Turn on the projector.

Point to the three blocks at the bottom of the screen. Say: **These blocks are the start of an attribute tower. I had a rule in mind when I put the blocks in the tower. Look at the small yellow square. How many ways is it different from the small red square?** (1 way) **Look at the small yellow circle. How many ways is it different from the small yellow square?** (1 way) **Look for a pattern. Work together and see if you can figure out my rule.**

Give the students time to find the rule. Then get ideas. Make sure that everyone sees that each block is different in one way from the block next to it. The second block is the same shape and size, but a different color. The next one is the same color and size, but a different shape. Then say: **Now look at these blocks** (point to the four blocks at the top of the screen). **Which one of these blocks should come next? Work with your partner.**

Give the students time to decide which block comes next. Then have a group share their solution. Add the block to the tower and then have the students record what the next block should be. Continue in this way until all the blocks are added to the tower.

Talking About Discoveries

Ask the students how they decided which block came next.

Solving More Problems

Have the students work in pairs. Give each pair a set of Attribute Blocks, paper, and pencils. If the students are working with the 60-piece set of Attribute Blocks, discuss the attribute of thickness.

Have the students make their own attribute towers. Have them use one-, two-, three-, or four-difference rules.

Attribute Puzzles

Getting Ready

- Use 1 set of Attribute Blocks for the Overhead Projector.
- Make a transparency of Puzzle Square (page 90).

Setting Up the Overhead Projector

- Put the Puzzle Square transparency on the projector.
- Put the blocks on the square as shown. Put the rest of the small blocks at the top of the projector.

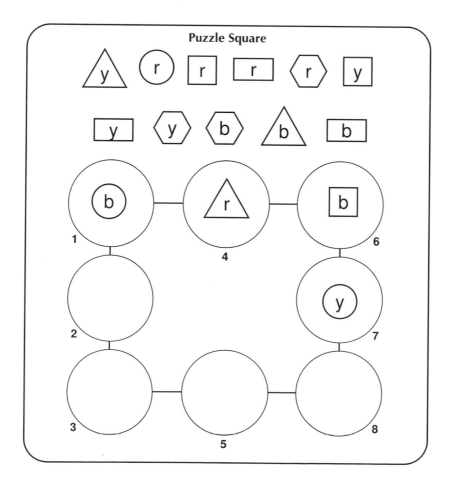

Solving Problems

Turn on the projector.

Say: **I used a rule when I put the blocks in this square. Look at each block and compare it to the blocks next to it. Look for a pattern in the number of differences between the blocks. Think about whether I used a one-, two-, or three-difference rule.** (two-difference rule)

Give the students time to discuss this. Have groups share their ideas for your rule. When everyone understands the rule (each block is different in two ways from the block next to it), say: **Look at the blocks at the top of the screen. Think about how many of these blocks would fit in the space marked 8. How many of these blocks would be different in two ways from the small yellow circle? Write your answer.**

Give the students time to record their answers. Then have them explain their solutions. (6) Tell the students you are picking one block, the small red square, to put in space 8. Continue in the same way, having them decide how many blocks will fit in space 5. (6) Put the small blue hexagon in space 5. Ask how many blocks will fit in space 3 (5), and then put the small yellow rectangle in that space. How many will fit in space 2? (1—the small red hexagon)

Talking About Discoveries

Ask students how they decided which blocks would fit in each space. Did this get easier after the first space?

Solving More Problems

Have the students work in pairs. Give each pair a set of Attribute Blocks, a copy of Puzzle Square (page 90), paper, and pencils. If the students are using a 60-piece set of Attribute Blocks, discuss the attribute of thickness.

Have each pair play the Puzzle Square game. Have them decide on a one-, two-, three-, or four- difference rule for their game. Players take turns putting a block anywhere on the square. Every block must have the right number of differences from the block next to it. Each correctly-placed block scores one point.

Circle Puzzles

Getting Ready

- Use 1 set of Attribute Blocks for the Overhead Projector.
- Make a transparency of Attribute Circles (page 91).
- Give each group of students a Think Sheet and a pencil.

Setting Up the Overhead Projector

- Put the transparency on the projector.
- Put the Attribute Blocks on the transparency as shown.

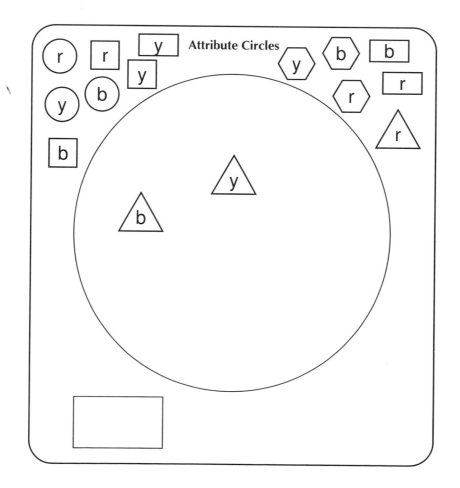

Solving Problems

Turn on the projector.

Say: **I had a rule in mind when I put these blocks in the circle. Talk together and see if you can figure out my rule. Record your ideas on your Think Sheet.**

Give the students time to write their rules, then have them share their ideas. When everyone knows that the rule is all triangles, draw a triangle in the box on the transparency. Say: **Which of the other blocks belong in the circle?** When they are ready, have the students share their solutions. Put the block in the circle. (△r)

Take the blocks out of the circle and erase the triangle from the box. Set up new problems by placing the following groups of blocks in the circle. Continue in the same way.

1. ⬤r ⬡r △r   Rule: all red blocks

      (Missing blocks: r r)

2. b y r b   Rule: all rectangles

      (Missing blocks: r y)

Talking About Discoveries

Have the students share their ideas for finding the rules. Ask: **How did you decide what the rule was? What did you look for? What did you discover about the blocks?**

Solving More Problems

Have the students work in pairs. Give each pair a set of Attribute Blocks, a copy of Attribute Circles (page 91), paper, and pencils. If the students are using a 60-piece set of Attribute Blocks, discuss the attribute of thickness.

Have students take turns making up Circle Puzzles. One student decides on a rule and puts a few blocks that fit the rule in the circle. Other players try to guess the rule by finding blocks that they think belong in the circle.

Mystery Squares

Getting Ready

- Use 1 set of Attribute Blocks for the Overhead Projector.
- Make a transparency of Puzzle Square (page 90).
- Give each group of students a Think Sheet and a pencil.

Setting Up the Overhead Projector

- Put the transparency on the projector.
- Put the Attribute Blocks in a square on the projector as shown.

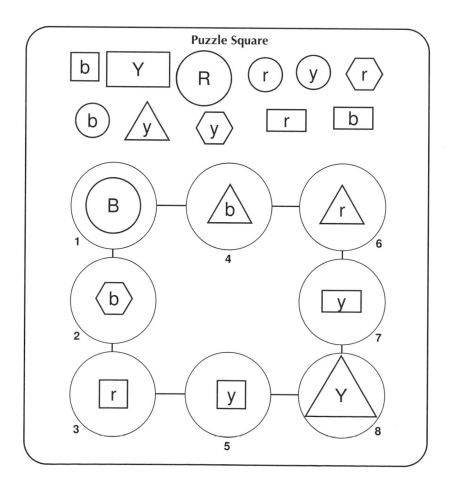

Overhead Math Discoveries, Grades 4-6
© 1993 Ideal School Supply Company

Solving Problems

Turn on the projector.

Tell the students that something is wrong with this square. Say: **The rule for this square is a two-difference rule. Every block should be different in two ways from each block next to it. Look carefully at the blocks and see if you can find blocks that don't fit the rule.**

Give the students time to look at the square and decide which blocks don't follow the rule. Then let the groups share their ideas. (Between 4 and 6, only one difference; between 3 and 5, only one difference)

After students identify the blocks that don't follow the rule, explain that you could take out either 3 or 5, and either 4 or 6. Remove 3 and 6. Say: **Look at the blocks at the top of the screen. Which of these blocks could we put in space 3. Write your answer on your Think Sheet.** Give students time to record, then have them share their answers. (⬜r , Ⓡ, or △r) Then do the same thing for space 6. (Ⓡ, ⬜r , or ⬡r)

Talking About Discoveries

Ask the students how they discovered the blocks that didn't fit the rule. What did they think about when they looked at the blocks in the square?

Solving More Problems

Have the students work in pairs. Give each pair a set of Attribute Blocks. If the students are using a 60-piece set of Attribute Blocks, discuss the attribute of thickness.

Have each pair make a Mystery Puzzle Square. Have them decide on a rule, find the blocks for the square, and then replace two of the blocks with blocks that don't fit the rule. Have each pair solve another pair's Mystery Puzzle Square.

Two-Circle Puzzles

Getting Ready

- Use 1 set of Attribute Blocks for the Overhead Projector.

- Make 2 transparencies of Attribute Circles (page 91).

- Give each group of students a Think Sheet and a pencil.

Setting Up the Overhead Projector

- Put the transparencies on the projector. Overlap the two circles as shown.

- Put the Attribute Blocks on the projector as shown.

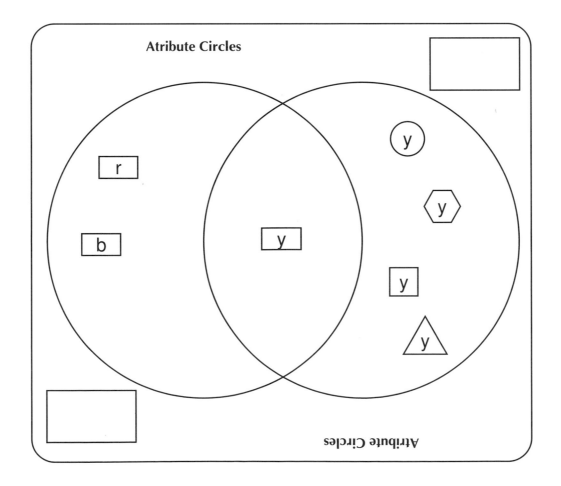

Solving Problems

Turn on the projector.

Say: **Now there are two circles. Each circle has a rule, and the section where the circles come together is called the intersection. Look at the blocks in each circle and in the intersection. See if you can figure out what the rule is for each circle. Write the rules on your Think Sheet and also a sentence that tells why the small yellow rectangle is in the intersection.**

When the students have finished, have them share their answers. Then draw a rectangle in one label and write **yellow** in the other label on the transparency.

Take the blocks off the circles and set up a new problem. Erase the labels, and put the blocks on the transparency as shown:

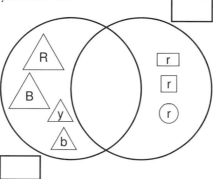

Divide the rest of the blocks evenly among the groups. Try to divide up the missing blocks. Tell the groups to look at this problem, think about what the rules are, and whether they have a block that belongs in either circle or the intersection. When the students are ready, have them share their ideas for the rules. (triangles and small, red) Mark these on the transparency. Then have the groups bring up the missing blocks.

triangles: /Y\   intersection: /r\

small, red: ⟨r⟩

Talking About Discoveries

Ask students to talk about how they figured out the rules for the circles. How did they decide what belonged in the intersection?

Solving More Problems.

Have the students work in pairs. Give each pair a set of Attribute Blocks. If the students are using a 60-piece set of Attribute Blocks, discuss the attribute of thickness.

Have each pair draw two large overlapping circles on their paper. Have them make a Two-Circle Puzzle. Have them decide on rules, find the blocks for the circles. Have each pair solve another pair's Two-Circle Puzzle.

Sums for Zim and Zor

Using _____ block(s) from each, how many sums can you show?

Overhead Math Discoveries, Grades 4-6
© 1993 Ideal School Supply Company

What's Left for Kron?

How many different ways can you subtract _____ block(s)?

Number Detective

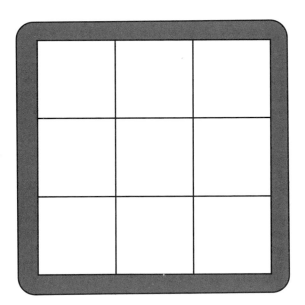

Overhead Math Discoveries, Grades 4-6
© 1993 Ideal School Supply Company

To the teacher: Permission is
given to reproduce this page.

Dr. Numo's Creatures

Dr. Numo

Partly Percents

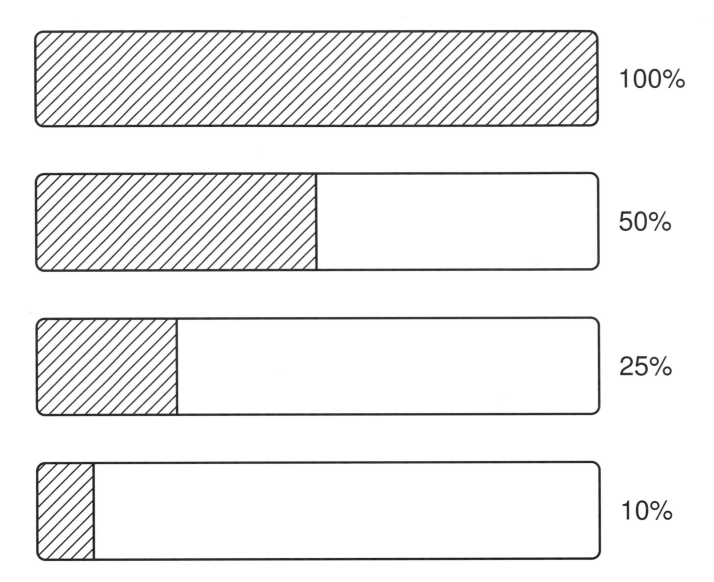

100%

50%

25%

10%

Overhead Math Discoveries, Grades 4-6
© 1993 Ideal School Supply Company

Money Mix

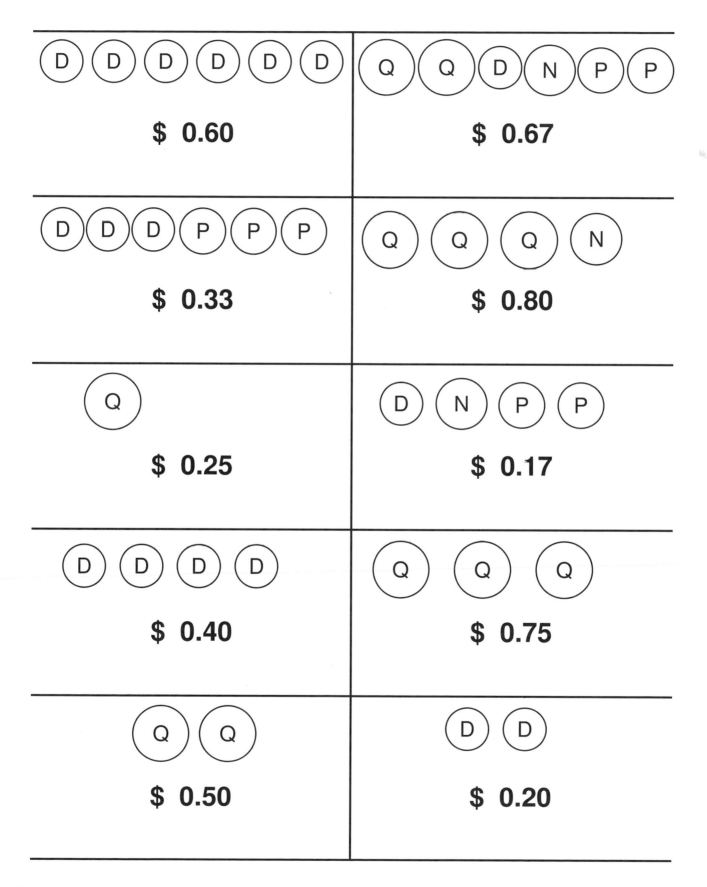

D D D D D D
$ 0.60

Q Q D N P P
$ 0.67

D D D P P P
$ 0.33

Q Q Q N
$ 0.80

Q
$ 0.25

D N P P
$ 0.17

D D D D
$ 0.40

Q Q Q
$ 0.75

Q Q
$ 0.50

D D
$ 0.20

Cutting Up Tangrams

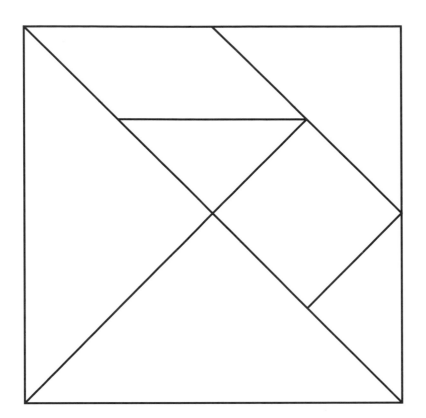

Overhead Math Discoveries, Grades 4-6
© 1993 Ideal School Supply Company

Angle Puzzles

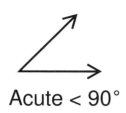

Acute < 90°

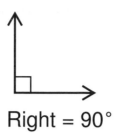

Right = 90°

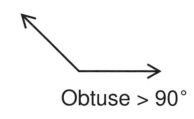

Obtuse > 90°

Spacey Shapes

Overhead Math Discoveries, Grades 4-6
© 1993 Ideal School Supply Company

Take a Turn

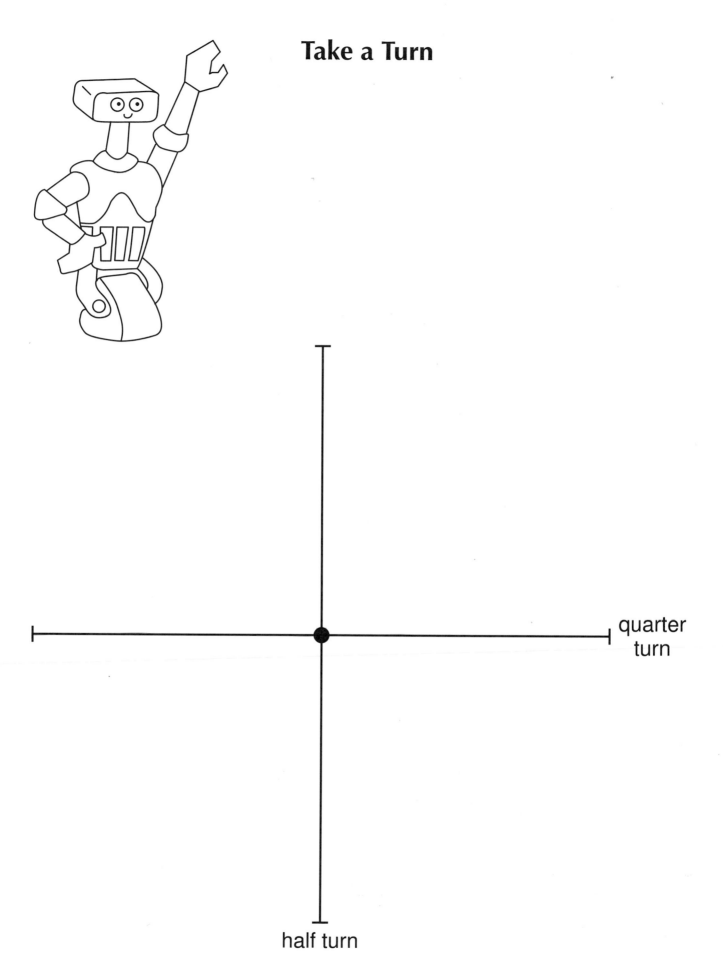

quarter
turn

half turn

Puzzle Square

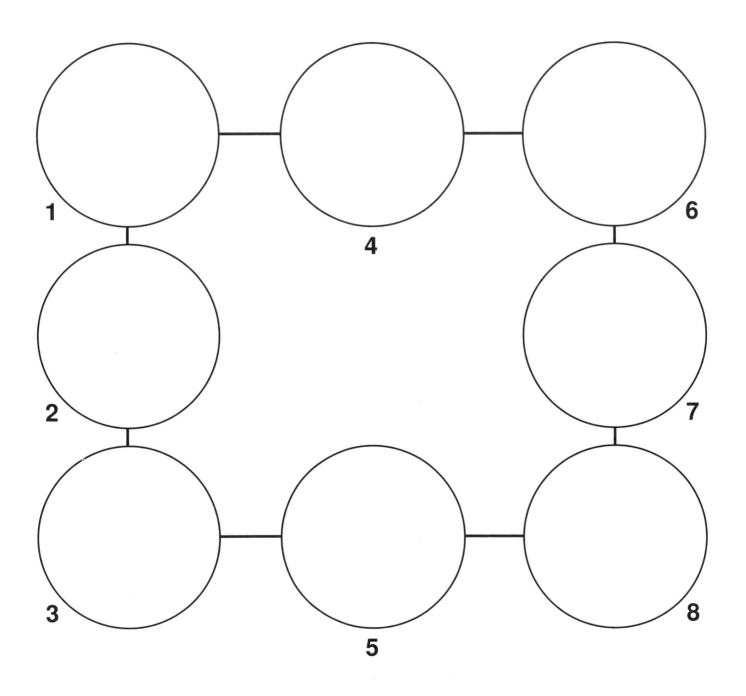

Attribute Circles

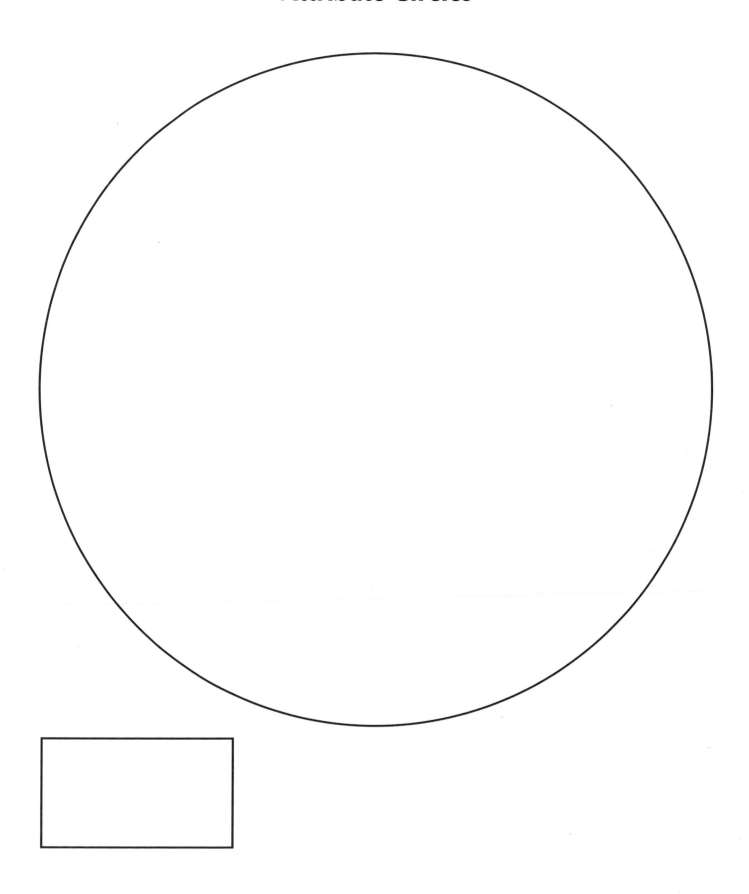

Overhead Math Discoveries, Grades 4-6
© 1993 Ideal School Supply Company